Robert McSweeney NOVEL

Maillet, Antonine. **The Devil Is Loose!**
Walker. Apr. 1987. c.310p. tr. by Philip
Stratford. ISBN 0-8027-0958-3. $17.95. F
This novel of lost innocence unfolds
in a Canadian coastal village during
the Depression and under the shadow
of Prohibition. The setting is signifi-
cant, for it allows the major conflicts
to develop: rural Canada versus ur-
ban America, the boldness of youth
(as exemplified by the lovely Crache
à Pic, literally "spit in your eye,"
skipper of her own refurbished craft)
against the sinister use of land, sea,
and people (as demonstrated by bootleggers Dieudonné and Al Capone).
The tone is deceptively light, for
these characters are cursed by obliga-
tions from the past that lend an eerie
sense of predestination to the story.
The translation from the French cap-
tures the flavor, humor, and pathos
of a novel that should appeal to pubic
library users. Maillet is the first
North American to have won the
prestigious Prix Goncourt.—*Joseph
Levandoski, Free Lib. of Philadel-
phia*

This is an uncorrected proof of a review scheduled for Library Journal, Apr. 15 1987

THE DEVIL IS LOOSE!

THE DEVIL IS LOOSE!

Antonine Maillet

TRANSLATED BY PHILIP STRATFORD

Walker and Company
New York

First published in the United States of America in 1987 by the
Walker Publishing Company, Inc.

Published simultaneously in Canada by John Wiley & Sons Canada, Limited, Rexdale, Ontario.

Library of Congress Cataloging-in-Publication Data

Maillet, Antonine, 1929–
   The devil is loose!

   Translation of: Crache à pic.
   I. Title.
PQ3919.2.M26C6813   1987   843   86-32542
ISBN 0-8027-0958-3

Printed in the United States of America

10 9 8 7 6 5 4 3 2 1

Original work *(Crache à Pic)* copyright © 1984 by Antonine Maillet. English translation copyright © 1986 by Philip Stratford and first
published by Lester & Orpen Dennys in Canada, 1986.

To the memory of Hervé Michaud

THE DEVIL IS LOOSE!

It was Old Clovis told the story to my father. He remembered it all happening. But they say that when he cocked an eye at the ways of the world his left pupil was more elastic than his right. Not only that, but his tongue was so rough and his gullet so rasping that words lost a vowel or two, or got their consonants jumbled as they came through. In passing it on to me, my father had no choice but to plane the sentences down and scour the phrases clean of moss and verdigris. And now I in turn pass on this true story to you, stripped of all verbal ornament or twist of wit. And I swear before God and his saints that my only intention is to distract my contemporaries from the misfortune of living at a time when, since everything is permitted, they will never know the multiple splendours of forbidden fruit.

Here, then, is the story I got from my father, who got it from Old Clovis, who got it by the dipper straight from life in the days when our fathers and mothers, denied drink by the laws of man, had to appeal to God, who raised up for them, among the marsh reeds and the dune hay, a bold and joyful race of smugglers.

Make the most of it, my friends, and welcome! As for me, I must return to my memories and my flasks.

CHAPTER ONE

AROUND ABOUT THE START OF THE THIRTIES, THE weathercock of the world suddenly began spinning like crazy. The winds blew willy-nilly, backing up on themselves, tossing one another upside down, meeting head on, jostling each other out of the way — the nor'easter splitting the sou'wester, the north wind caught up in a tornado that came out of the south in search of the centre of the world. Yes, at the start of the fourth decade of this century the world was looking for its own centre all right.

Well, it was a complete waste of time. Pure foolishness, all that chasing right and left, east and west, up, down, inside, outside — much too much of it. For the answer was to abandon the chase, grab hold of the wings of the weathercock, and look straight down, right down to where, all in a day's work, a handful of gallant, canny heirs of the Depression were battling tooth and nail to tame the winds.

Right there off the Atlantic coast of Canada on that first day of August 1930, her arms wrapped round the mainmast of her schooner, braving the waves splashing into her face, a pretty wench named Crache-à-Pic stood laughing and shouting headlong into the wind:

"I got him!"

The waves were running twenty feet high that night. And the sky was as wild as the sea. The horizon, already torn to shreds by the waves and the witch of a wind, had now been swallowed up by the night. The one solitary thing moving on the strait between the islands and the mainland was the schooner, hurled from crest to crest and fighting stubbornly not to sink.

"I got him!" shouts Crache-à-Pic even louder. "I got him good!" cries the master of the Sea-Cow, daughter of a long line of giants, sorcerers, and intrepid sailors.

Crache-à-Pic and her improvised crew — made up of neighbours, her godmother, her brother, and his foster-brother — got their baptism in North Atlantic rum-running that night. And they outsmarted the boss of the Gulf, big Dieudonné, into the bargain — Dieudonné the smuggler, who had laid down the law along every inch of coast from Newfoundland to Maine for the last ten years.

With the sou'wester raging in her ears, Crache-à-Pic can't hear what the fifty-year-old Twins, her mother's neighbours, are yelling at her from the fo'c's'le . . . something like, "Let go the shrouds, get down out of there!" What's he saying, that Dagobert . . . or is it Adalbert . . . what's he want? She opens her mouth to reply and gets a slosh of foam in the gullet. As Adal . . . Dago . . . as Adal-Gobert waves four arms to signal something to Crache-à-Pic . . . swoosh! a wave breaks over the bowsprit and explodes in a spattering of salt.

God! What a night!

The rest of the crew is crawling on the deck clutching at stays and pulleys and pitching wildly with the schooner as she sweats salt brine from every seam. But though the waves break over Crache-à-Pic's head and cascade down her back, she remains standing. "The rest of the crew" is that matched set of old bachelors, Adalbert-Dagobert, welded together heart and soul by fifty years of sharing the joys and miseries of a life at sea and the two or three hundred words that make up their cultural heritage; "the rest" is also Céleste, a hefty matron with a well-hung jaw and an endless stream of jokes and saws, and ready to shower you with them on the slightest excuse; and finally, "the rest" is those two foster-brothers and bosom pals, each barely twenty years old: Céleste's boy, quick and nimble Jimmy-the-Flea, and Crache-à-Pic's innocent younger brother, Tobie. So there you have them, cursing the heavens and steering through the night — the whole crew of the *Sea-Cow*, commanded by a long-legged girl with a turned-up nose, a mane of windswept blonde hair, and a pair of blue eyes that would take your breath away, the last of the line of Crache-à-Pics.

The story of Crache-à-Pic and her *Sea-Cow* was a real romance. She had dug the schooner up two months before, in the shipyard of a dealer in second-hand hulks and rigging in the backwater of a little port on Cape Breton. The ship was nothing more than a carcass of twisted ribs and planks, oozing moss, creaking in mast and pulleys, shrouded in her own sail; but for Crache-à-Pic, who had just returned from a trip round the world in the galley of an ocean freighter, it was love at first sight. And now, after two months' conditioning, the wanton thing responded like a lamb. She would roll on her beam ends, shimmy from head to toe, write wild arabesques with her wake, and send fountains of sea spray spurting into the air while groaning with pleasure in every joint. And in the evening, cockpit soused and sails sundered, she would heave to at the Cap-Lumière dock, dead beat but with her mast high, and proud as a pope.

On this particular August night in 1930 she has every reason to be proud, the hussy, and Crache-à-Pic is laughing and stroking her mast. One of the ancient Twins is yelling something, his words twisted by the wind, scraps of sound mixed with the faint noise of a motor that Crache-à-Pic hasn't heard yet. . . . What's he want, old Adal-Gobert? And she laughs again at the wild beauty of the angry sea, the kind of sea you love to be out in with a ship like this, especially tonight when Crache-à-Pic has struck her first blow. Yes indeed! For this very night she has foiled both the law and the great Dieudonné, she has beaten the bootlegger at his own game and beaten the law at. . . .

What's that?

She cups her hands around her mouth: "Louder! I can't hear!"

She freezes, listens, just picks it out: the growl of a motor. The motor of a launch. She recognizes it, though the wind shreds the sound and scatters it over the water.

"The coastguard!"

They must be very close—but where? The sound comes from everywhere at once. What's got into them to come out on such a night? And in whose honour, poachers or bootleggers?

"Douse the lantern . . . and the running lights."

She lets go of the mast and bounds across the deck like a deer. The Twins join her, crawling on hands and knees. Jimmy-the-Flea comes back slithering on his belly. And Tobie, rolling with the swells, buries his head in his sister's lap while she, with an instinctive gesture, takes his neck in the crook of her arm . . . don't you worry, little one . . . and cocks her ear into the wind.

No doubt about it, they're there all right, a quarter of a mile away, she can hear them. Off to port. Got to get the sail up. Clear out of here. This is no time to have the schooner searched.

"The sail!" she yells to the Twins.

But they drop their mouths open as one, without uttering a single sound. Hoist sail in this banshee of a wind? She's crazy, Aglaé's daughter is, crazy!

"Let's get out of here," she insists. "Put some distance between us. We can hear the cutter, but they can't hear our sails. . . . Let's use our advantage while it's still night."

And she takes hold of the halyards.

Just get a few hundred yards apart — the sail will hold for such a short haul — and let the launch go its own way. But now the roar of the motor, thrown about by the winds, can be heard from both port and starboard. And the sail won't hoist. Jimmy suggests waiting at least till the squall passes, till they can see which side the coastguard's on. Crache-à-Pic refuses.

"When we see them, they'll see us too. If they catch us. . . ."

One of the Twins, the one who hasn't gone down to the hold, leans forward and shouts in Crache-à-Pic's ear:

"Better pitch everything overboard . . . and damn quick!"

Oh no! Not that! Crache-à-Pic won't hear of it. She seeks out Ad . . . Gobert's eyes in the gloom. That — never! Jettison the whole cargo of wine from Saint-Pierre and the Napoleon brandy snatched on the high seas in the teeth of Dieudonné, boss of the bootleggers? The first real exploit of her career, and you think she — the heir of the Crache-à-Pics — will toss it into the sea? Think again!

She had known since midsummer, since the Feast of Saint John the Baptist, that something was afoot. Dieudonné had been so cagey, had muffled his plans in such mystery and silence, that the secret had finally filtered through the cracks

between the four points of the compass. A whisper here, a
sly look there, a word between clenched teeth . . . and Zéphirine, sister-in-law of Célestine, Céleste's cousin, had done
the rest.

Zéphirine was the Dieudonnés' servant, and every day
she swept up choice scraps of information along with the
crumbs from their table. The eve of the feast of La Saint-
Jean there was a fine wine from Saint-Pierre and Miquelon
to wash down the chicken, and it was in the dregs of the
glasses that the servant collected this pearl.

The eve of La Saint-Jean, well adrift in the Saint-Pierre
wine, the boss of the smugglers had heard his own voice
gurgle the words that for months had been pampering his
vanity: "President . . . the President of the United States."
Just at that moment his wife had clinked her fork against her
gold tooth. The president? The American president? Had
her husband reached the heights of dealing with heads of
state, then? And she felt a mouthful of chicken breast catch
in her gullet. This churchworthy and patroness of good works
never meddled in the business, straight or devious — business
is business — of her husband's gang. But a president? Even
the archbishop would have turned a blind eye to a black-
market deal in such high places. Had Dieudonné really said
the President of the United States?

Zéphirine was the only one at the table who didn't
choke on the news. First because she had neither a gold
tooth sunk in a piece of chicken breast, nor wine from Saint-
Pierre in her gullet, but mainly because she was the most
trustworthy, fiercely loyal, and close-lipped woman the coast
had ever known, virtues which had won her her place at
the Dieudonnés'.

She would never unseal her lips. Except to her sister-
in-law Célestine.

And from Célestine to Céleste to her son, Jimmy-the-Flea, the best-kept secret in the whole history of bootleg-ging plopped down one fine morning on the deck of the *Sea-Cow*.

In three sentences Jimmy-the-Flea had summed up the whole affair to Crache-à-Pic:

— The American president escaped twice a year to a cottage hidden in the woods on an island lost somewhere off the Canadian coast.

— The president, like any self-respecting man of the world, was a great lover of wines and cognac imported from France.

— And since his predecessor had signed the Prohibi-tion Act, the president, for his own reasons, preferred to get his supplies from outside his home country.

Enough said! Crache-à-Pic could guess the rest.

The very next day she set her own grapevine to work, and through the cousin–to–sister-in-law–to–servant connec-tion, from Céleste to Célestine to Zéphirine, reached the Dieudonnés' kitchen where she learned the day, the hour, and the place of delivery. Also the password. Or its equival-ent. For kitchens, even the Dieudonnés', are none too famil-iar with historical figures and heroes from France, and for "Charlemagne", which seemed to Zéphirine a preposterous invention, she had substituted "Charlie Man" as more in line with the lingo of the smuggling trade.

Towards noon on the first day of August 1930, Dieudonné heard the nor'easter begin to moan and real-ized that neither he nor his men would set out to sea that night.

"Let's hope the crew from Saint-Pierre and Miquelon stays in harbour too!"

And between his teeth to his henchman Black Willy:

"From Saint-Pierre, and from Cocagne as well."

Black Willy roared with laughter. From Cocagne! Why, those patched-up hulls with their three-horsepower engines, the sea would swallow them up in a gulp. When Dieudonné's *Kouchibougouac* stays tied up, every vessel around, whether it runs by sail or by oars or by some tin-pot motor, knows it's no time to take to sea. No matter where you're from — Cocagne, Grand-Digue, Champdoré, or Sainte-Marie-des-Côtes — it's all the same, the sea's the sea.

"And right now she's wild. The devil is loose!"

Dieudonné's brow darkens. He's not in the habit of defying the elements. All his life the old fox has known how to keep his footing amid obstacles and profit from adversity. But this time he grinds his teeth. He's been preparing this deal for months. . . . Everything ready, plans well laid, wheels well oiled. . . . And then damned Nature has to interfere and send him a dog-day gale! If only it doesn't last too long! Not more than two days. Have to warn Saint-Pierre and Miquelon. And the patrol round the president's island, too. And at the same time find some way to distract the coast-guard . . . for another day or two.

"Constable Martial don't know a thing yet," says Black Willy.

"Knows nothing for certain, but suspects something for sure. Acts like a man with fleas in his long-johns."

"Have to send him off to scratch someplace else," replies Black Willy.

"Yes, somewhere out of our hair."

Black Willy draws his head back into his shell, then whistles.

"What about after Crache-à-Pic?"

The two men stare at each other, then with one accord

slacken their cheeks. Black Willy has seen his chief's right eyelid quiver and knows the day is saved. When Dieudonné's eye trembles, the whole coast shudders.

"Spread the word from barn to barn, from forge to fish-shed, that Crache-à-Pic means to go to sea tonight, foul weather or not."

Black Willy hesitates an instant.

"You think Martial will bite?"

Crache-à-Pic, a woman under thirty, at the helm of a makeshift schooner with her ragged crew of misfits at sea on a night like this? What officer would believe that?

Dieudonné lets slip the little laugh he saves for his better days.

"He won't bite, but he'll still have to go out and keep an eye on her. Where there's smoke there's fire, he'll say. If word gets out that the bitch has taken to sea, Martial will try to figure out what that means, and he'll take off and follow her . . . from Home Sweet Home to Lovers' Lane."

And glancing up at the weathercock spinning madly on the gable of his barn, Dieudonné stepped across the threshold and into the loft where he hid his telegraph, in a cave hollowed out under the hay.

As he went through the door he just happened to meet Zéphirine laden down with two buckets of frothy milk.

Black Willy's rumour about Crache-à-Pic's plan to put out to sea that night did the rounds of the village all afternoon. And by milking time it reached Martial, first officer of the county. It was Marie-Pet who elected to deliver it to him in person, all done up in lisps and insinuations and bad intentions.

Marie-Pet, widowed and in her sixties, had lost all her

front teeth one after another; they had melted away in the homemade fudge she sold from door to door. Consequently she lisped. And since in her piety she never spread scandal in more than a whisper, so she wouldn't be accused of having an evil tongue, her murmured lispings obliged the sharpest ears to strain to the utmost, which made Marie-Pet the best-listened-to gossip in the parish.

"Crache-à-Pic meanth to thet out to thea tonight."

The coastguard could not choose but hear. Once again Marie-Pet had scored a point. When she left Martial she knew that the wildest devil of a wind wouldn't prevent the officer from doing his duty that night, and that Crache-à-Pic would have to straighten her mast and iron her sails flat.

That night, sure enough, Martial moved out.

His launch was faster than Crache-à-Pic's schooner, but less supple and less yielding. Now, in stormy weather all a vessel can do is yield and abandon itself, nonchalant and trusting, and let the sea make the first move and enter into its dance. Crache-à-Pic, practically born at sea, had always known this. So the *Sea-Cow* had a head start on the cutter: Crache-à-Pic had only to follow the waves; the officer had to follow Crache-à-Pic.

And he couldn't follow her long, for while his motor launch bucked and stiffened in the waves, the sailboat — never even suspecting she was pursued — let herself be tossed and tumbled, all the time crowing with pleasure.

Guided by instinct alone, and carried by the accomplice waves . . . take them or leave them . . . that night the pretty little schooner, known locally as a shipbuilder's reject, was to carry Crache-à-Pic and her joyful crew into the heart of the most amazing and amusing adventure in the history of rum-running. For the *Sea-Cow* was headed out to sea, sailing almost blind to a rendezvous with a foreign coaster riding with her engines shut down and looking suspiciously as though she were waiting for someone.

Crache-à-Pic could see the captain on the fo'c's'le shouting curses at the sea, the filthy weather, and his crewmen working on the deck. She saw that he'd seen her, and hearing him call, "Drop the ladder!" she lost not a second but caught the line thrown her and fixed it round her waist. Then in turn she yelled to the foreign captain that she was coming aboard. But at the very moment she jumped, a treacherous wave drew the two ships apart and left poor Crache-à-Pic spreadeagled in mid-air over a sea that would have made the boldest quake. Her muscles stretching to breaking point, her heart in her mouth, she had thirty seconds to read L-A S-I-R-E-N-E on the bow of the coaster and to hear a voice above demand the password.

"Charlie Man!" she wrenched up from a throat as rough as a washboard.

The captain seemed to hesitate, weighing the syllables. But on the high seas, in raging waves swept up in sixty-mile-an-hour winds and hurled like a wall against the hull, "Charlemagne" could easily be confused with "Charlie Man". The fate of Crache-à-Pic didn't hang on such a trifle.

It hung on her luck, her instinct, and her courage. But chiefly on her pluck. In a wild sea, on a filthy night, this girl of twenty-seven spat and swore like a man, ordering the foreign smugglers to roll the barrels and hoist the cases — "Quick now, lads" — to the deck of her astonished schooner.

In later days Clovis the storyteller, in one of those hiccoughing asides that were his trademark, used to say that at that instant the whole country heard, from above the clouds, the gusty laughter of old Charlemagne himself.

Then the coaster started up its two engines and headed back to the islands of Saint-Pierre and Miquelon, leaving behind the *Sea-Cow* and her precious cargo of wine and cognac destined for the President of the United States.

While Crache-à-Pic's schooner had been playing out its destiny on the high seas, the officers' launch pursuing her had three times met near-catastrophe. First in stupidly running into a pod of whales lost and terrified in the storm and in no mood on such a night to dispute claims about the limits of territorial waters. Then in coming within a hair's breadth of breaking up on the rocks of Prince Edward Island buried under thirty-foot waves. And finally in insisting stubbornly to remain at sea when the sea herself kept multiplying her warnings. But Martial stuck to his guns.

"A woman takes to sea in that leaky ark and you expect the coastguard to stay safe in harbour? What sort of a chicken would that make me?"

Bent double on the bridge, reeling and puking his guts out, he seemed the most miserable, pig-headed man ever spawned by the sea. And as if the sea took pity on him, suddenly — in the trough of a wave right under his nose — she threw up a vision that left poor Martial and his crew with their jaws sagging. For there before them, all sails flying and decked out as if for a wedding, danced the schooner in the heart of the storm.

"In the name of the law, stop!" he managed to shout.

And the schooner came nuzzling up alongside and dropped her sails to the foot of the mast like the most innocent little girl in the world, who has already eaten all the jam and has nothing more to hide.

Nothing more to hide, either in her hold or in her cabin, for before giving herself up the *Sea-Cow* had taken great pains to stow away the prize haul she had made that night. In the short half-hour fate had allowed between Adal-Gobert's "Pitch everything overboard" and the officer's summons, "In the name of the law!" Crache-à-Pic had noticed floating around her vessel, like manna fallen from heaven, a dozen buoys with red and black pennants.

"Holy Mother of Jesus Christ," she cried, "lobster pots!"

And shoving and punching, she drove her men up to the bow of the schooner.

"Throw the lobsters back in the sea," she ordered, "and Tobie and Jimmy go get the cases of wine and line them up on deck!"

The maritime Twins, who had known this heir of the Crache-à-Pics since her birth and had watched her grow and prosper, looked at one another and caught on at the same instant. Together they broke out in a short hoarse chuckle.

So while the officers' launch contended with wind and wave a few fathoms farther on, the *Sea-Cow* was hauling up dozens of traps from the deep, exchanging lobsters for wine and cognac, and dropping the traps back into the briny with no one the wiser. Then Crache-à-Pic took the tiller and tried to put some distance between herself and the coastguard cutter she had just spied, thrown up on the crest of a wave.

"Heave the lobsters overboard," she barely had time to shout to her crew.

But this time her crew took the bit in their teeth. A storm at sea sharpens the appetite — and they were famished. At the sight of those great beasts, livid green and wriggling for all they were worth, Adalbert, without consulting his twin, lifted the lid of the great kettle that Céleste always kept simmering on the stove. Seeing this, his twin, in a spirit of fraternity, stuffed several of the creatures into a straw mattress. Not to be left out, Jimmy-the-Flea popped a couple into his boots and strung them up on the chain of the lamp; and finally Céleste, short of ideas, threw two big males into the hollow of a coil of rope and sat on it. The whole operation was complete in less time than it takes to tell, and Crache-à-Pic, who was already lowering the ladder for the coastguard, hadn't a clue what they'd done.

Up they come, the three representatives of the law — Martial the chief constable, a young assistant, and a fisheries officer — and setting foot on the deck of the *Sea-Cow* they present themselves with their usual courtesy:

"In the name of the law!"

"Nobody move!"

"Your papers!"

And the three dive into the cabin.

Now begins the most burlesque hunt in the officers' career. Wedged in between hammocks, portholes, coils of cable, barrels of flour, frying pans, stewpots, and oilskins hanging from nails, our legal representatives hardly know what to look for or where to begin. But any schooner out at sea at night in a tempest must be trafficking something. Even if she's all alone out there. Even if her only cargo is cables, straw ticks, and flour. And even if the search turns up nothing, this nothing must be camouflaging something else. Up-ending benches, emptying boxes and barrels, the officers sniff their way around under the noses of a crew frozen as stiff as so many vestal virgins.

Only Crache-à-Pic is relaxed, calm and, to show her good will, bold enough to turn over mattresses, blankets, clothes, and old rags lying on benches or in corners. She's enjoying herself.

"Serve the visitors tea, Céleste. They look worn out."

"T-t-tea?" Céleste lets a pair of blank eyes roam vacantly over every rafter in the ceiling.

But what's got into them? Come on, Twins. . . . Come on, Céleste, you know as well as I do that the bottles are safe in the cooler at the bottom of the sea . . . what's wrong with you? Let the officers search . . . it'll teach them a lesson.

So then Crache-à-Pic decides to act like a captain, and taking a ladle down from its nail growls between her teeth, "Adalbert, there's water boiling on the stove."

And she reaches the dipper over in the direction of the Twins, who peer at each other wondering which one's called Adalbert tonight.

You could hear a fly land, or the hands of the clock turn. The weather, which has blown like fury all night, suddenly seems to stand stock still in the hold of the *Sea-Cow*. Nothing stirs, not a blessed thing . . . except for a mattress crawling across the floor of the cabin, writhing like a bundle of snakes. . . . And Céleste, who starts jerking up and down on her seat, seized by a strange fit of hiccoughs. "Eee! Hee!" And Jimmy-the-Flea, hanging his boots back on the lamp chain when they keep on falling on his head. The Twins are passing the ladle back and forth between them as though it were a hot potato, and poor Tobie, his eyes starting out of his head, stands there sniffing the fragrance of seaweed and salt water that's beginning to invade the cabin, that's also reaching Crache-à-Pic's nostrils, who at last catches on. . . .

The lobsters!

And raising her eyes to heaven to take God as her witness — what boneheads, what an idea! — she sees a large, egg-laden female swinging above her head, clamped by its claws to the lantern.

"Jesus and Mary!"

The oath escapes despite her and she hastens to smile at Martial, who squints in reply and screws up his lips. But before he has time to open his mouth, a boot comes loose from a rafter and drops at his feet jigging like a thing possessed. He leans over it, but Crache-à-Pic moves faster and with a kick sends it flying into a corner. There's one boot that won't be coming to its senses for a while.

But now it's the fisheries officer who seems to be coming to his. He too starts sniffing the air, making out a familiar aroma rising from the kettle and beginning to edge out the smell of wet wool and damp wood.

Crache-à-Pic watches as he seizes the spoon hanging over the stove and lifts the cover of the pot. Then the officer, to his great surprise, fishes out of the depths a woollen sock that Céleste had put to boil in soapy water.

The first laugh springs from the throats of the Twins, followed by Crache-à-Pic, then Jimmy, and finally Céleste, fused to her coil of rope, jigging and shouting as though her fanny were on fire. The officers stand wide-eyed and speechless, staring at this collection of ragged clowns who find nothing better to do, on a schooner adrift in a stormy sea, than boil their socks.

Martial sits down and attempts to regain his dignity. Turning to cast a compassionate eye on these poor benighted maritime adventurers, he says, "Drop anchor and I'll take you on board."

Crache-à-Pic looks him straight in the eye. "What for? Since when is it illegal for a schooner to go out at night?"

"Not illegal, but dangerous. I can take you ashore."
She laughs in his face.

"Want to bet my schooner will reach harbour before
your cutter?"

The officer's mouth drops open.

"Don't say I didn't warn you," he says, leaving the
Sea-Cow.

And before he starts up his motors, he hears through
the waves, "I'll count up to ten . . . the first one to the
dock. . . ."

The splendid gale of laughter that rose from the schooner
reverberated right to shore the next morning. But it wasn't
the same ones laughing. For after the sun had risen, some-
what late in the morning, a lobster-poacher's boat could be
observed making for port, zigzagging from one wave to
another, oars balancing on either side like a trapeze artist
on a high wire.

Melchior was standing on the aft thwart haranguing
the fish and his two pals, Pierre and Paul — nicknamed Gaspard and Balthazar to make up the trio of the Three Kings
— who lay glassy-eyed and singing in the bilge.

". . . not a single lobster, no, not a bloody bitch of a
one in the traps. The herrings ate them all. . . . Ever see
that, a herring swallow a lobster whole, shell and all? . . .
No, you never saw it, well me neither, so it must be whales
or turtles. . . . "

Gaspard and Balthazar look up, puzzled. Then a roar
of laughter rises from all three, for they've just lived the most
glorious morning in their lives. Not a single lobster in their
traps, more's the pity! But the turtles must have pissed in
the pots as a fisherman's tip, pissed a royal water, a divine
tithe, an intoxicating miracle, like that water that was changed

into wine. And the three drunks burst out laughing again, slapping the sea on the back with their oars.

"Can you tell me who the devil the holy son of a bootlegger is who sends us a Christmas present like this smack in the middle of August?"

Back in the thirties lobster-poaching was practised on a grand scale. Only two officers against Cocagne, Grand-Digue, Village-des-Trois-Maisons, and Sainte-Marie-des-Côtes, plus a dozen little improvised ports up as many creeks and bays ... it was like Gulliver against the Lilliputians. The poor representatives of the law were victims of a tacit general plot among the local fishermen, who might be enemies during the fishing season, but in off-season were only too happy to bat the officers back and forth like a ping-pong ball. When Grand-Digue put out to sea, Cocagne would act shifty and guilty; Champdoré would only leave port if screened by provocative hints from Village-des-Trois-Maisons; while Sainte-Marie-des-Côtes sheltered every departure from Bois-Joli, Cap-Lumière, or l'Anse-aux-Outardes with psst ... shhh ... ho-ho — which drove the fisheries officers wild every year between mid-July and the tenth of August, when lobster was out of season.

The day after the dog-day tempest Old Clovis went down to the shore very early, as usual, but waited in vain for the poachers' return. They showed up around noon, in full sunlight, without taking even the most elementary precautions. They came in singing:
    Passing through Paris,
    Downing my drink . . . ,
shouting their joy to the heavens in a boat reeling across a

strait still rumpled by last night's waves—a boat three sheets to
the wind on a dishevelled sea.

Old Clovis's eyes pop.

"Lord Jesus!" he says. "What's got into them jackasses?
The officers'll be down on them in no time flat. Sure got to
be dumb!"

The fishermen, laughing and slapping each other, pommel Old Clovis too as he stands there shaking his head,
wrinkling his brow, and flaring his nostrils in an effort to
understand.

But he understands quick enough when, lifting the
tarpaulin spread out in the bottom of the boat, he sees three
or four empty bottles . . . and dozens of others full of wine
and Napoleon brandy.

After the departure of Martial and his crew, to let on she
was playing the game, Crache-à-Pic gave orders to hoist the
sail and join the race. The Twins stared at her in dismay.

"But . . . the nor'easter . . . the sail will split from top
to bottom . . . and besides. . . ."

"And besides, we'll just let on," Crache-à-Pic corrected them. "Make Martial think we're going to meet him at
the dock. . . . Poor sap, he'll be so glad to think that though
we were on his tail he got there first just the same."

And she laughed at her own compassion and generosity. . . . Generosity that would cost her dear that night, for in
moving even a few hundred yards away from the buoys under
that coal-black sky, they had lost sight of their lobster pots.

"Holy Columbus! Where the devil . . . ?"

But the devil wasn't telling; snickering and sneering,
he hid the little red and black flags in the folds of his cloak.

" . . . Bear left, right . . . to starboard . . . no, port. . . ."

The Twins whip the ship, which sweats and snorts in frustration; Jimmy-the-Flea hangs on to the tiller like grim death but his cries of "Haw!" and "Gee!" are all in vain. His breathless mount pitches in the wind, yawing to and fro, yanked now by the nor'easterly blow, now by a fresh young sou'-wester that's springing up. Crache-à-Pic can't believe her heart. She coddles and caresses her *Sea-Cow*, lavishing words of tenderness and encouragement on her, telling her to hold on, to trust the sea, to rely on her flair, her intuition.

"Come on, little white cow, don't buck so, you'll find them, it was just about here, remember, you recognize the spot, there were plenty of rocks on the bottom, you could tell by the white caps breaking over them . . . look for the red and black flags . . . on those little pine floaters."

Crache-à-Pic refuses to let the schooner give up. Port! Starboard! Straight ahead! A little to the left! What is it, Céleste? The old girl comes up from below with an armful of rags. No time to swab the decks now, Céleste . . . no time for polishing brass. . . . And then, casting her eyes on her godmother's bundle, Crache-à-Pic understands. The flags! The red and black flags, neatly detached from their buoys and hidden in the hold. . . .

" . . . under a pile of blankets."

Crache-à-Pic holds her breath. Who could have done it? But then she sees her brother Tobie standing beside her, wrestling with the terrible choice whether to tie his bootlaces around his knee or knot them at the ankle. She swallows back the gob of saliva blocking her throat and: "Take those rags back to the hold, Céleste, and don't tell the others."

But the others have already seen and understood. They're all staring at their feet. That poor innocent Tobie must have heard his sister tell Jimmy or the Twins to get the schooner away from the flags, not to let the officers see them. It was so much simpler just to take them off the buoys and hide them. Tobie always did go straight to the simplest solution.

He lifts his head towards his sister and suddenly feels miserable: because of the sad look in Crache-à-Pic's eyes; because of Céleste who's scolding her son, jaunty Jimmy-the-Flea, to keep him from opening his mouth and grinding his teeth.

Suddenly the sky lightens, as if day is about to break. Tobie hears a laugh that starts gurgling in his sister's throat, escapes between her teeth, and breaks pealing out over the sea. He's saved. Everything's all right again. When Crache-à-Pic laughs, the world spins like a merry-go-round. She doubles up, holding her sides before the startled eyes of her crew, she chokes with laughter and between snorts bursts out, "The robbers are robbed and ribbed for their robbery," and laughs so hard that little by little the others are shaken loose themselves, chuckle by contagion, and then burst into guffaws. Tobie is so glad to see it that he laughs too, in short little spasms.

The storm is over. The sea gives a long shudder of exhaustion after its rage of the night before. And when at last, about five o'clock, the red ball leaps to the eastern horizon and strikes the sea like a gong, and the shepherd's star twinkles and is gone, then finally the *Sea-Cow* can let her hull settle into the trough of the waves that will rock her to sleep.

Crache-à-Pic has cast her shadow over big Dieudonné and his gang of smugglers and has revealed to the world the inside and the underside of the trade. From now on the big dealers will have to reckon with the small fry. And the long boots rising to the knee — which gave their name to the "bootleggers" — will know from now on that a bunch of broken-down galoshes are on their trail.

"Galoshes!" she cries. "From now on we'll take the name 'Galoshes'. And I say that from this day forward the bootleggers will have to reckon with us — the Galoshes of the *Sea-Cow!*"

And she pats her schooner's flank.

Jimmy-the-Flea, his mother Céleste, the Twins Adal-Gobert, and even innocent Tobie, raise their arms to the sun in a sign of assent. But the sun overpowers them. One after another, the arms drop to the deck, dragging down the exhausted bodies that have fought all night against the elements and fate.

Jimmy-the-Flea is snoring already; then the Twins in two-part harmony; then Céleste with her head stowed in the hole of a life-preserver; and finally Tobie rolled up like a foetus in Crache-à-Pic's lap. She alone keeps her eyes open, caressing the nape of her brother's neck and musing.... Poor little fellow! A tough life for a kid. But he's a man already, going on twenty-four . . . still, a man who'll remain a child all his life. Not crazy, not an idiot, just innocent. And Crache-à-Pic's thoughts plunge back into the past.

She was three years old. It's her most distant memory. That day she had invented a new game, giving names to the pebbles she had collected and grouped in a family, almost a village, arranging them according to size and colour, lining them up and distributing tasks and titles, without regard to merit or justice but according to her own sweet will, like God granting favours to his favourites. She was remaking his creation.

All day long Little Whirligig — that was her nickname at the time — remade the world to her measure.

But that evening her father didn't come back home as he usually did. Her mother called for him a good part of the night, and by morning her call had changed to a long lamentation that rocked the child's troubled sleep. They didn't give her father a real funeral, since he was lost at sea, but performed a primitive and grotesque sort of ceremony around the empty boat that had drifted back to port.

Next day, their neighbour Céleste brought over a chicken stew, johnny-cake, and hot milk. Little Whirligig heard a conversation between the two women that became more and more heated, with Céleste calling her mother thoughtless and stubborn.

"Think of the children," she kept repeating.

At that her mother hugged her three little ones to her apron fit to strangle them — Crache-à-Pic, and her two brothers Roch and Colas who were seven and eight, almost men.

"At least think of the little one on the way," Céleste added.

At three Little Whirligig already knew a lot about many things — tides and shells and seaweed, whales and ants, wild plants and berries in the woods. But she was totally ignorant of her own origins. She knew that her brother Roch had been left by the Indians, and that Colas had been found under the porch steps, but as for herself, she'd come from nowhere. They'd told her dozens of stories about her coming from cabbages or swallows' nests, but that was just it, there were too many stories; they ought to have fixed on one. So she rejected them all.

And now here was her godmother Céleste announcing the arrival of another. Where did she get her information? The little girl went off to sulk in a corner. It was then she remembered the baby next door. Céleste herself was feeding a newborn who had been blown into her house on the morning breeze, brought by the crows. A baby all pink and wrinkled, that looked like nothing so much as some kind of intruder, but one Céleste cuddled and cooed over as though it was her very own. So Céleste knew her way around babies, and it was all right for her to talk to her mother that way. And Little Whirligig came out of her corner.

She had already forgotten this incident when one night she dreamt that someone was lifting her out of her cradle and laying her on a bed. And next morning she woke up to find herself squeezed in between her two brothers, to the strident cries of a new baby.

Little Whirligig owed her nickname to her bubbling, impulsive personality. By the age of three she had already conquered and occupied half the family territory: the house, the outbuildings, the barn, the shed for fishing tackle, the kitchen garden, the rhubarb patch, the stream, and the back field. And this morning they had the nerve to wrench her out of her own cradle and toss her into someone else's bed. It wasn't fair!

Céleste, who as chance would have it had stopped by at their place during the night, was the first to welcome the new baby who had been left under the front steps by the Indians. But since Céleste had found it at the Crache-à-Pics' place she had no claim on the child; he would be a Crache-à-Pic like Little Whirligig, Roch, and Colas. They named him Tobie.

And that's how she who would come to bear the glorious name of Crache-à-Pic lived out the coming of her little brother.

She strokes his hair and muses that he didn't have an easy childhood, this posthumous child, and that his head may bear the scars of it yet.

After bringing Tobie into the world, Crache-à-Pic's mother went ahead with her plan, despite Céleste's protests and the *curé*'s reproaches. She rigged out her late husband's boat, crammed her four children into it, and put out to sea. The sea was calm and gentle and led the bold soul to believe the gods were on board and all would be well. And that night she came back to the jetty with fifty pounds of lobster.

"The devil's mixed up in this!" the two twins Adalbert and Dagobert, neighbours on the other side, said in one breath. A woman lobster fisherman? Such a thing was unheard of on the coast.

It was unheard of in the whole of America. A woman not yet thirty, with a child at her breast and three kids in her skirts, leaving each morning before dawn to haul in her traps! Good weather and bad, Crache-à-Pic's widow would stow her little ones in the bottom of the boat and grab hold of the oars.

"At least they won't die of hunger," she'd say to Céleste, coming back at night.

And Céleste finally had to agree she was right.

But one day the sea showed its teeth, on seeing a school of whales driven into the strait by icebergs, and the fisherwoman realized she would have to redouble the strength of her giant arms. She made the two little ones fast to her waist and ordered the older boys to stay hunched in the bilge with their arms round the thwarts. Every time a whale calf strayed from the herd she would push it towards its mother with the oar, before the rest of them took it into their heads to look for the stray. That evening she came into port completely exhausted, her hands bleeding, and said nothing to Céleste about her adventure.

Yet next day she was back at sea, her brow as resolute and fierce as ever.

Then at the end of September she had to face her first storm. Her neighbours the Twins had warned her the night before that the weather was turning foul, that perhaps she had better not risk it.

"What are you talking about? The sun set red as fire."

But the weathercock on the barn roof was swinging strangely — as though nervous and out of kilter — and the sea was too calm. When the surface is smooth as oil, beware the ocean swell.

She laughed in the Twins' faces, for this giant of a woman had learnt to mistrust men more than the elements.

"If I don't get back, come after me to see where I've gone," she told them.

Adalbert and Dagobert later told Crache-à-Pic that they'd waited all morning down by the port, their eyes fixed on the fog bank, and that at noon they'd put out to sea themselves. But the storm had drawn the Crache-à-Pics' boat beyond the strait, out to the open sea beyond Prince Edward Island.

Crache-à-Pic remembers singing and shouting for joy that morning while her mother fought with all her might to keep her tribe on board and prevent the boat from capsizing. Little Whirligig threw insults to the wind and defied the waves:

Do your worst
You hunchback sea,
You'll never get
The better of me!

And the sea answered her impudence by hurling jets of water in her face. Her head snug in a woollen cap rimed with salt, she just laughed all the louder. But her older brothers, less plucky and more aware of the danger, held their tongues and tried to help their mother in every way possible. Roch pushed on the oars, while Colas tried to calm the terrified baby.

Towards evening, fear slowly began to touch the little girl. She had been bold as brass as long as she could see her mother struggling. But night fell on the tiny lost boat like the shadow of the ogre on Tom Thumb, and even the mother's courage failed her for a moment. The child felt it and trembled for the first time that day.

An hour later Colas called out that he'd seen a star fallen into the sea.

"There, in the trough of the wave! There!"

And the Twins, who since midday had been waving their lantern shouting "Crache-à-Pic!", at last heard the children's voices in echo:

"Here we are!"

Baby Tobie had his first epileptic fit that night, and the next day Céleste easily made her neighbour see reason. From then on the widow took her two boys to sea with her and left the new baby to nurse with Céleste, who chortled,

"Where there's enough for one, there's enough for two. The Good Lord fitted us out for twins."

And Dagobert-Adalbert blushed in unison.

As for Little Whirligig. . . .

She left neither mother nor godmother the time to dispute the care of her small person. She jumped into the boat, clamped her arms around the oars, and waited there scowling. Her mother, Aglaé, saw that if she didn't want another epileptic fit on her hands. . . . So she took her daughter out to sea.

From that day onward the Twins' boat followed in the wake of the Crache-à-Pics', for the loyal neighbours refused to leave their fearless friend to her own devices.

"Tomorrow they're calling for fifteen-foot waves," they'd come to announce at her back stoop.

At first the widow would get angry or laugh in their faces, but at last she gave in. Under their scarecrow-like exteriors those two twins had hearts of gold. She knew them capable of creating thunder and lightning themselves to keep her from setting sail under a leaden sky. They would hide the oars, the anchor, the painter, her sou'wester, or the children . . . anything to protect her against her own boldness. And when all else failed:

"If your man was alive, Aglaé, he wouldn't let you go out today."

It was the Twins' ultimate argument, heavy with unction and consequence.

"If my man was alive," the widow would reply, "I wouldn't have to go out today . . . or ever again."

But she gave in, sure at any rate that with such chivalrous friends in attendance she would always have something to feed her little ones. And the Twins heaved a sigh of relief.

One evening they spent longer than usual wiping their

feet on the doormat, then barged forward, shoving each other mutually in the back. From the window Colas reported to his mother that one Twin had his chin buried in a bunch of daisies, while the other had his nose in a bouquet of wild roses. With a chuckle the widow stepped up to open the door to the two, who simultaneously thrust their arms forward, filling the doorway with roses and daisies.

"Come in," she said, curious to discover which Twin was behind which bouquet.

It wasn't as simple as all that. The two bouquets were mixed already, the thorns of the roses scratching the stems of the daisies while the latter dropped pollen on the petals of the former — intermingled and mixed like the Twins themselves. The widow had to thrust her hand through the mass of stems, leaves, and flowers to reach a face to caress, and even then found both identical.

"Smells like springtime," she said, and grabbing a neck at random forced its owner to be the first to enter.

Little Whirligig inherited the flowers and ran through the house strewing petals everywhere while Roch and Colas, their legs hanging between the bars of the attic staircase, played *she loves me . . . she loves me not* with the daisies.

At thirty, Aglaé Crache-à-Pic was a superb colossus of a woman. Too beautiful for mediocre men, too big for your common or garden male. Shaped by the gods for a Crache-à-Pic . . . or for a set of twins.

Twins? The giantess couldn't suppress a chuckle. Was she supposed to double up, then? Stutter out "Y-yes" to two demands for her hand at once? She felt sure that neither of the Adalbert-Dagoberts, despite the strength of their love, would resolve to speak first for fear of cheating the other.

An impossible love which the two lobster-fishing Twins were to share for twenty years.

Twenty years on the open sea, each night bringing back a meagre catch of cod, mackerel, or lobster, depending on the season, which almost absentmindedly they would leave on the Crache-à-Pics' porch. And Aglaé, smiling just as spontaneously, would ask them to stay to supper . . . just this once.

Which is why Little Whirligig and her brothers were never deprived of a father's love.

Time went by.

Then one day Roch and Colas announced to their mother that a schooner in harbour was hiring longshore-men. Aglaé got the message. That same evening she pre-pared two duffel bags, stuffing them with woollens and socks and razor blades and bandanas and pipe tobacco and two yellowing photographs of big Crache-à-Pic, their father. The Twins explained in vain the meaning of longshoremen; Aglaé continued her packing just the same, knowing in her gut that when a young man fifteen or sixteen sets foot on the deck of a schooner one morning, that night he's likely to sleep in a hammock.

"When you've got the sea in your blood on both sides of the bow. . . ."

She was thinking of her own blood, flowing out of Saint-Pierre and Miquelon, as much as Crache-à-Pic's whose forefather had heaved up over the horizon in the crows-nest of a ship from the Old Country one fine day. Then, smiling at the Twins, she added:

" . . . on all three sides of the bow!"

Adalbert and Dagobert took the youngsters down to

the harbour next morning. But that day, though the weather was fine, Aglaé didn't go to sea.

Then it was the turn of Little Whirligig. No simple schooner for the only daughter of the Crache-à-Pics. A cargo-ship. A long, low, smoke-grimed steamship, piercing the fog with its seductive whistle. The young girl felt her veins swell with salt blood.

"Just one short trip round the world," she said to her mother, "and then I'll come back home. I won't let you die alone."

. . . .

She kept her word and came back in time to bury her mother.

Later on she swore to Céleste and the Twins that she'd heard Aglaé's voice threading the winds of the Pacific, and had realized she'd have to hurry. So she secretly abandoned her freighter for a passenger ship, and that for a three-master, and that for a whaler which dropped her off in the little Cape Breton port where she unearthed her *Sea-Cow* in the second-hand shipyard. She landed one morning at the village jetty just in time to collect her mother's last laugh and these words which she offered, tickling her daughter's neck:

"I've made preserves of wild strawberries, currants, and gooseberries from Dieudonné's fields. Eat all you want, don't think twice about it, because Dieudonné stole those fields from poor folk in the first place."

Next day the widow Aglaé didn't wake up; to her daughter she left as heritage a younger brother, Tobie, a collection of sheds and shacks around a broken-down house, a fishing boat that for twenty years had carried to sea the pluckiest heart on the coast, and the name Crache-à-Pic which for three generations would threaten to burst the old storytellers' sacks stuffed with legends of the sea.

Stretched out on the foredeck of her schooner, the wild child of the seas caresses the nape of her brother Tobie's neck while the rest of her clan, the intrepid Galoshes, snore on around her. She smiles at their slumber, and searches for the link that will join her future to her past. Then, moving her legs, she feels the hobble that will keep her tied: her young brother. She will never again sail on a cargo-ship or liner. Henceforth her ocean will never reach beyond those islands that dot the Gulf like stars in the firmament. Her share of the inheritance — a saltwater pond bigger than a province, but smaller than her dreams.

And Crache-à-Pic lifts her nose to the heavens, sniffing and defying them. She has received her baptism of the sea tonight, at the hands of a witch of a wind, and her baptism of smuggling at the hands of a captain from Saint-Pierre who will have to do a lot of explaining to Dieudonné tomorrow.

A few hours later, one by one the Galoshes opened their eyes to the raucous song of the sea-poachers slapping the waves with their oars to the rhythm of their yodel-ay-ee-oo's. The Twins cupped doubled hands to their brows and peered in that direction; Céleste shook Jimmy's fleas up and he jumped to his feet like a cat; Tobie snorted awake, and Crache-à-Pic, narrowing her eyes, recognized the boat of handsome Melchior the poacher.

"Sweet Mother Mary!" she exclaimed, "our bottles!"

That's right, Crache-à-Pic, the president's wine cellar.

All those vintage wines and Napoleon brandy in the hands of the lobster-poachers. Crache-à-Pic howled to the sea at the top of her lungs that she was a stupid bitch, and the whole race of fishermen wasn't worth a fart from an unfrocked, constipated priest!

Then she threw herself on the deck pummelling the Twins in the ribs, using them as a punching bag as her mother had so often done before. Little by little they calmed her down, reminding her that the whole coast had a healthy thirst, that fishermen were a great race, that the main thing was to spoil the smugglers' game and stop them getting rich at the expense of everyone else in the village, that next time. . . .

Céleste added that in any case they'd soon get even, for the poachers wouldn't get off as easy as that . . . just let them turn up on shore and you'll see what's left of their prize catch when the officers get their hands on them and. . . .

Suddenly Crache-à-Pic grasps her head in both hands: she's just remembered Martial.

"Got to find a way to warn those fishermen," she says.

She sees the Twins smile, and reads their thoughts. They too have just realized what side their team will be on from now on: against the law and against the bootlegging racket, but with the freebooters. The Galoshes will have their fun playing between the two, spreading laughter, liquor, and song among their starving countrymen.

While the crew of the *Sea-Cow* were wishing them luck, our three poachers resolved to cross the village at high noon, guided by Old Clovis pushing a wheelbarrow covered by a piece of salt-eaten canvas. It was his idea to take the bull by the horns. According to him, the main street which cut the village in two, north and south, would be much safer than any cowpath or sidestreet, all of them watched more closely than the Tower of London in these bootlegging times. No one, from Marie-Pet to the nun's hired man, would have let pass unchallenged a wheelbarrow pushed by four stout fellows tiptoeing down a back alley. Ah, no! Better to risk the whole shebang, and take the village on face to face in broad daylight. That was Clovis's opinion.

"Hello! . . ."

"Nice day! . . ."

Nobody move! Here's Marie-Pet. Pretend to be looking somewhere else.

But Marie-Pet isn't pretending anything. Her beady eyes are fastened on the canvas.

"Whath that you're thelling thith morning that thmelth tho bad you've got it buried under a pieth of oilcloth?" lisps Marie-Pet.

And her arm unwinds from her wide sleeve like the neck of a heron. Clovis grabs it in mid-air and begins pumping her hand warmly.

"I forgot to thank you, Marie Caissie, for . . . for your generosity."

And he shakes her shrivelled-up claw all the harder while Marie-Pet, who lays claim to every virtue going except generosity, seeks a glimmer of enlightenment in the depths of Clovis's eye.

"My daughter Agnès tells me," Old Clovis rushes on, "that you were the first to sign up as a volunteer."

Volunteer for what? And Marie-Pet's eye continues to quiz the old man, who is now scratching his brain with the full force of his imagination.

"Weren't you the first in the parish a few days ago . . .

34

or maybe it was a few weeks ago . . . I can't remember . . .
time flies so fast nowadays . . . to have the idea of a benefit
picnic for the poor?"

Marie-Pet gasps for breath; Clovis, too, for that matter.
A picnic in the parish, and she didn't know a thing about
it? And to find out like this, last of all, and from the mouth
of an old ne'er-do-well about as interested in church affairs
as a pumpkin in a procession of ants! Must be one of the
doctor's wife's ideas, I do believe, or the priest's servant's,
the old bag. Well, if they think they're going to get away
with that!

"Count on me, Clovith," she retorts, gathering up her
skirts. "I'll be right there in the middle of that picnic, and
the poor won't want for a thingle thing."

The wheelbarrow starts up again a little too hastily,
emitting a gracious and joyful clink of bottles.

"If you ask me, the parish will get its picnic before the
end of summer," says the first fisherman to begin to sober
up.

Now the wheelbarrow heads into the slope that leads
to the forge. Only a hundred yards left before the first safe
resting-place — buck up, me boyos!

The blacksmith's shop is the personal private property
of Old Clovis himself, who has transformed it into his home.
Nobody on the coast would dream of searching somebody's
home, not even if he was looking for his father's corpse.
The country just doesn't function that way. A home's a man's
castle, and it's sacred.

Except to the officers of the law.

But Old Clovis is not involved in either smuggling or
poaching. He just watches the crows and wild geese go by,
and time itself, driving men on towards their destiny.

"In your forge, Clovis . . . we'll hide the stuff in your forge," grunts the drunkest of the poachers, with a superb burp which sets the ear of the doctor, just behind them, quivering with curiosity.

"The forge? What's cooking up there now? That forge is used for just about everything except shoeing horses."

All four of our joyful companions let drop the handles of the wheelbarrow, which lands with a clatter and a brisk sound of clinking glass, like hail on a tin roof.

The doctor of Sainte-Marie-des-Côtes, something of an expert in flasks and flagons, casts a twinkling eye at Old Clovis, the only one sober enough to despair of the situation. But Clovis never despairs for long; life is too short. And returning the doctor's smile, he deplores the misery of hard times reducing strong healthy men to combing ditches and fencerows in search of empty bottles. "Just think of it, doctor! Times are so bad that old seadogs like these have to go selling empty bottles from door to door like a bunch of kids — it's a crying shame!"

The doctor offers a "Tsk . . . tsk" in sympathy and doesn't even ask to see the bottles; instead he is the soul of generosity.

"I always need bottles for my remedies," he says. "Bring me around a dozen or two."

And over his shoulder:

"Empties, of course!"

Old Clovis, seeing the doctor stride away, slaps his thigh and lets out a "Holy smokes!"

The forge is now only a stone's throw away, three turns of a wheel or so and. . . .

"Can I have one?"

A little kid of five or six, stretching up to the top of his full forty inches, has his eyes glued on the bottles which, from being so bounced and bandied about, are sticking their necks out of every hole in the barrow. He stands there between the wheel and the single step leading up to the forge, his nose dripping, his eyes greedy, and his hands in his pockets up to the elbows.

Clovis is just about to tell the little snot-face to go get his mother to blow his nose, when he hears the rumble of the giant Joe Colossus bearing down on him. In a flash the old tar snatches the wee lad up with one hand and sets him on top of the pile of bottles.

"Hold tight, laddie, I'm going to give you a great wheelbarrow-ride."

And while the three poachers slink around behind the forge, Old Clovis grabs the two handles himself and shouts to his horse,

"Giddap! Giddap there, Nellie! Gee! Haw!"

. . . to the delight of the Allains' bastard kid, who suddenly sees the whole world beginning to turn into his dreams.

"If I was Agnès, I wouldn't let my father live all alone in the forge," says the *curé*'s servant at her kitchen window. "That Old Clovis is going round the bend. . . . Look at him now, playing hobbyhorse with a brat who's not even properly churched!"

But the little bastard is sitting pretty on his steed and wouldn't change places today with any well-born offspring of the bonds of holy matrimony. Astride his glass horse, he casts a haughty, scornful look on the legitimate world below.

"Haw! Gee! Giddap!"

When Old Clovis, finally out of breath, is obliged to stop, he sees that he has passed the church, circled the convent, and come to a halt at a gate in the fence that encloses the cow-pasture. The forge is as small as a doghouse in its patch of ferns. And no sign now of either the poachers or the colossus of a bootlegger. So Clovis takes the little fellow by the elbow and lifts him off his horse.

"Thanks, laddie. Now go find your mother," he says.

But the child is still too thrilled and dizzy to budge.

"Go on," Clovis insists gently. "Your mother will be worried about you. . . . What did you say your name was?"

"Gène"

"How's that?"

"Eugène-à-Maria."

"Ah! Yes, that's it. Well, go tell Maria that Clovis-à-Clovis says, hello. Go on now, quick, be off with you, Little-Next-to-Nothing."

And Little-Next-to-Nothing, proud of his new title and sure that hereafter life will always be good to him, smacks his fanny and shouts,

"Giddap, Nellie! Giddap!"

. . . and gallops off over the hills and the sand dunes.

"And now," says Clovis, mopping his brow, "I'll have to find me a pick and shovel."

And with his finger to his lips he tells his Dobbin not to move, to wait for him right there. Then, on tiptoe so as not to disturb the stones on the road, he sets off towards the convent barn.

Joe Colossus, unwilling to resign himself to returning empty-handed to Dieudonné, prowls around the forge several times. And each time he trips over the feet of the three card-players sitting round an upturned molasses barrel, sucking on clay pipes blacker than a stove-pipe.

"Hello, Joe! Great weather after such a stormy night, eh? . . . Play your queen, you jerk!"

The jerk plays his king.

The giant continues his search without answering, sniffing every pile of lumber and sack of wheat, kicking over this or that heap of odds and ends decorating Old Clovis's forge. Ignoring him, the card-players continue to joust with blows of queen, ace, and jack.

"If you've got clubs, Gaspard, don't forget they're trumps."

"I've got more clubs in my hand than there were stars in the sky last night. But the sky's kind of sobered up since then, as you might say. . . . Hey!"

The yelp follows a kick in the shin, and the blabbermouth feels the eyes of his two pals burning a hole in his tongue.

"Play, Melchior, you stupid bugger. Shut up and play."

But Joe Colossus is already on top of them. He stands over the barrel, which rocks under his heavy shadow, and smells all three.

"What's that you're stinking of this morning, Melchior?"

The third Wise Man keeps his mouth clamped shut so as not to stink further.

It's Balthazar who speaks up for him.

"He ate too many beans last night. He's been farting all morning."

Joe Colossus grunts scornfully. His muzzle is keen enough to tell the difference between the smell of a fart and a bottle.

The card-players look out the window, scanning the

horizon for the silhouette of Old Clovis. He's disappeared, lock, stock, and barrel. Suddenly Joe Colossus drops his eyes to the molasses barrel, the only piece of junk he hasn't knocked over yet because it was already upside down.

"What's that keg there hiding?"

The Three Kings blink in the sun.

"Nothing," says Melchior.

"Nothing?"

"It's empty."

"Hmm . . . mind if I just take a look?"

Joe is getting a little playful now he knows he's getting hot and his prey won't escape him. But Melchior needs to gain time . . . time for Clovis, that is. . . .

"It's molasses," he says with a triumphant swoop, covering an eight of spades with a seven of diamonds.

Whereupon Gaspard scoops up the trick under the astonished eyes of Melchior, who seems past distinguishing either numbers or suits.

"Molasses?" growls Joe Colossus. "Let's see. I want to taste some."

"Can't you read?" risks the king of the Three Kings, playing double or nothing with his queen of hearts. "It's written on the barrel."

But the barrel flies into the air before the queen can land on the jack. Instinctively the three card-players jerk back. The barrel is empty, completely empty, hiding nothing more than an anthill whose inhabitants scurry off to left and right while the going is good.

"Holy Goddam Jesus Christ!" swears Big Joe, and stomps off to rejoin Little Philias, the Damien boys, and the rest of the bootlegger clan.

It really wasn't the giant's day.

"There's my ten of diamonds, and bye-bye to your ace," says Melchior.

The other two stare at him in amazement.

"But I thought we were playing whist!"

And they burst out laughing so hard they almost wet their pants.

A few minutes later Old Clovis turns up singing *A la claire fontaine* and pushing a wheelbarrow full of empty bottles.

"Clovis! What did you do with it?"

The three friends examine the contents of the wheelbarrow incredulously. Dozens of bottles gape uncorked, lying there helter-skelter, the neck of a Père Anselme snuggling up against the butt of a Napoleon. . . .

"It can't be true!"

How, in less than an hour, had he. . . .

So Clovis settled down to tell them all. First he had got rid of the kid . . . poor little shaver . . . Maria Allain's bastard, you know, the little surprise that arrived after that Norwegian cargo-ship came in for a load of saw-logs . . . yes, well, Maria's kid. Then he'd thought of a safe place. He'd borrowed a pick and shovel from the Sisters' barn to dig a hole with, then just when he was about to bury the bottles, he'd thought of the doctor's offer. . . .

"Ah, screw the doctor!" Balthazar interrupted.

No, no, Clovis had a better idea. It was what he called his two-in-one shot. First undeceive the doctor, the sly dog, who wouldn't believe his eyes; second . . . after all, an empty's an empty and they sell three for a cent, which makes four cents a dozen . . . and a cent's a cent in times like these. . . .

"In the convent henhouse I found a couple of great

little barrels, almost new. They only smelt a little of chicken feed . . . I gave what was left to the pigs. Nobody saw me. I buried the barrels and saved the bottles. The hardest thing was getting the corks out without breaking the necks."

Clovis reserved his three horrified friends one more jolt:

"Now come along with me to the doctor's," he said.

. . . Hmmm. . . . Bad business all that, Clovis. A lot too many precautions and a lot too many detours. . . .

"Are you sure nobody saw you?"

"Sure? There was a great gang of witnesses. They all saw, ogled, had a fine snoop. At least twenty or thirty of them!"

"What!!!"

The Three Kings were within an ace of jumping on Clovis.

"A whole herd of cows and their calves."

As Clovis had predicted, the doctor seemed very surprised to find them knocking at his door with a full wheelbarrow of empty bottles.

The welcome Black Willy gave his underlings was a preview of the reception in store for all of them from their supreme commander, Dieudonné: a multicoloured fit of rage ranging from green to blue, to red, to violet.

. . . The American president's wine cellar, just think of it! Disappeared, melted into the mist of the Acadian coast! A selection of the best wines and cognacs, sealed and packed with the greatest care, and safely stored in the cellars of Saint-Pierre and Miquelon, and all so it could end up where?

"In Crache-à-Pic's skirts!"

And Black Willy, anticipating and imitating his chief,

held his head and pounded his forehead with his fist:

"A fat lot of good it does to have bright ideas!"

When Black Willy told his boss the news, even though he had taken the trouble to dress it up and smooth out the rough edges, he stood stupefied at his chief's reaction. Before exploding in fury Dieudonné had taken the time . . . three seconds . . . to meditate on the real reason motivating Crache-à-Pic. What had set her off? What was the one word too many, the phrase that had stuck in her gullet and thrown her in his path? Then he understood. The heir of the Crache-à-Pics, fresh from her travels, had taken off to sea on a storm-ridden night because a little worm of an apprentice bootlegger had sneered at her "schooner sailed by a woman".

Upon which the bootlegger grabbed Black Willy by the throat and, nose to nose, growled,

"Next time you have one of your bright ideas, go sell it to Polyte Lévesque."

Little by little Dieudonné calmed down and began to calculate his losses. Quite a sum for a single night. But there were still a few hours left in the day. Still time to track down the lost prize. From Crache-à-Pic to the night-fishermen, to the day-fishermen, to those who lived by snooping and prying open others' secrets, still time to follow the trail to those cases and get them back before the village had time to get drunk.

"Put everybody on pick-and-shovel duty, Black Willy, and turn the country inside out before sunset. By nightfall I don't want to see a single haycock or sand dune standing right side up."

When Black Willy transmitted the chief's message to his men, he put two fingers on the hands of his silver watch:

"You're lucky it's still the middle of summer. You've

got four hours before sundown. And Dieudonné wants you
to know he has no intention of going to sell herring to the
U.S. president tomorrow. Get that clear in your heads."

One thing was clear all right. Those who were fired
that morning were rehired that afternoon. And they each
drew breath again, but not too deeply, aware of the mission
they had to fulfil in less than four hours.

"Now all I need to know," said Dieudonné, "is who
was fiddling around with my telegraph wires last night."

And striding off towards the barn, he met Zéphirine
bringing the milk in as usual.

The weathercock of the world, which had spent the whole
summer trying to reconcile contrary winds and take up
its station right over the centre of the globe, suddenly
perceived a second child of this age stepping forth like
Crache-à-Pic — left foot foremost for luck — into a new life.
The weathercock stopped, winked, and let fly a splendid
cock-a-doodle-doo so loud it made Old Clovis look up in
wonder. Really — he told my father so himself, some years
later.

Since his birth in the heart of New England, Ti-Louis
the Whistler had also been trying to plant his foot in the
centre of the world. But in 1930 a strange presentiment
came over him. His soul yearned for the north, for a land
he hadn't seen since the day he came into this world — a
land whose memory he had received, along with his breath
and his heartbeat, from a mother who died in childbirth. It
stayed in his mind as a land rich in clover and marsh hay,
one that humped its back against the winter snows but let
all the pores of its hide swell open in springtime to drink in
the ice-melt and the first dews.

Alone, an orphan without father, mother, or country, knowing nothing of geography or the lore of the woods, on the day of his seventeenth birthday there was Ti-Louis the Whistler striding calmly towards the centre of the world.

Then, suddenly, the winds stopped in their tracks and were silent and the weathercock stood still. The great migratory birds, ready to fly south, switched direction and began to wing north, sensing that the warmer part of the globe was there.

Ti-Louis who had been walking for eight to ten days, stopped to scrape the mud from the sole of his boot and was surprised to find nothing there but paper, a layer of paper that gave way under his nails to reveal a hardened flapjack that smelt vaguely like wool. His Aunt Flavie had knitted these socks for him two years earlier. Two years! Even a great-aunt should know that a hungry boy is still growing at fifteen; that two years is too long for one pair of socks; that hunger makes your kidneys ache, and that makes your feet swell; that a young guy on his own doesn't wash his socks every night when he's mounting the Atlantic seaboard on foot; and that, to sum it all up, life's a pile of shit.

"A pile . . . of . . . shit!"

He didn't really believe it, but he shouted it out just the same to test his lungs and windpipe. Once or twice an hour he would try out his voice, his throat, and especially his tongue, with the dirtiest words he knew, just for the pleasure of ear and palate.

"Life's a pile of shit!"

Ti-Louis the Whistler wasn't born in a feather bed and had never tasted a mother's milk. He'd never had clean sheets and diapers either, not this kid. He'd opened his eyes on the world from the bottom of a wicker basket one day in 1913

— on a world creaking on its hinges, groaning in its door-jamb as it swung open on the Great War. Now, seventeen years later, Ti-Louis gave out with *Malbrough s'en va-t-en guerre* and *Marianne s'en va-t-au moulin*, songs that only his mother had sung. You'll recall that, in giving him life, his mother gave up hers — so by his birth he enriched the world with a large dose of ancestral memory transmitted navel-to-navel.

"This kid's belly bulges like a little treasure chest," his father liked to say. "Touch his bellybutton and out comes a song."

A belly like a treasure chest! Ti-Louis smiled at the memory of his father, who'd coughed up what was left of his lungs two years before in a Massachusetts pulp and paper mill where he'd gone to make his fortune. At fifteen the son was alone in the world. No family, outside of old Flavie who lived on the outskirts of Boston and had taught him his prayers and knit him his socks, and the vague memory of an aunt on his father's side who had stayed in the ancestral home-land up there on the Atlantic coast of Canada.

Sainte-Marie-des-Côtes.

For fifteen years his father had nourished the child body and soul with the names, now caressing, now pung-ent, of the country of his birth: Grand-Digue, Pré-d'en-Haut, Champdoré, Bois-Joli, Cocagne, Village-des-Trois-Maisons, Anse-aux-Outardes, Sainte-Marie-des-Côtes. And on rainy days thick with nostalgia his father would half-close his eyes and push back the horizon even farther, to beyond those faraway islands of Saint-Pierre and Miquelon. A country the shape of a necklace whose pearls fell one after another into the little belly-treasure-chest of Ti-Louis the Whistler. And the day of his father's funeral he knew that he'd always known he would have to go there.

But to get to that country from the outskirts of Boston he had to cross two states and a border. Add to that certain tactical errors which had twice led him south when the freight train he had jumped branched off in that direction twenty or thirty miles farther on. And that's how he came to find himself in New York's Central Station.

"Yes, I slept in a New York hotel," he shouts two years later, at a jack-rabbit sitting up expectantly on its hind legs.

The rabbit takes off in a bound for a heap of dried leaves, shocked at the thought of New York and preferring to sleep at home.

"On a bed of coal," Ti-Louis adds for himself, since there's nobody left to impress.

He spent a night in the cellars of the Hotel Astoria.

"It was December. I was freezing to death."

He remembers everything, the two years as a vagabond wandering over highways and byways, through fields, towns, and city streets; being bounced from doss-house to home for delinquents; nights in the park, meals out of garbage cans, broken shoes and worn-out socks. Two years between the death of his father and reaching his father's country.

He had jumped from the boxcar before the train actually reached the station. He was frozen stiff. It was two or three days before Christmas. He remembers because of the lights on the little Christmas trees. Because of *Jingle Bells* coming out of the Hotel Astoria each time the revolving door swung round. And mixed with the Christmas carols out came puffs of heat to wind round the neck of Ti-Louis the Orphan, as he stood there like a fencepost warming his eyes on the fur coats that brushed by him.

"Move, you bum!" a liveried valet suddenly shouted,

shouldering him aside so that he spun through the revolving door.

Ti-Louis's rags drew little attention in the great lobby of the hotel, where a fancy-dress ball was in progress. That is how he was able to reach the coal cellar and fall asleep there, as drowsy as a woodchuck expecting to spend the whole winter in his burrow.

"I woke up next morning to kicks in the bum."

The janitor of the hotel, who had taken him for a black, alerted the manager, who called the police, who extracted the poor Whistler from his pile of coal to throw him in prison. And there, dousing him with buckets of cold water spiked with javel, they discovered that he was white, not black, and that he wasn't even sixteen. So they sent him to a State Farm for rehabilitation.

But in the first third of the century these American collective farms contained too much uncleared land and too many untended animals to leave the guests of the state much time for rehabilitation. So Ti-Louis the Whistler wisely decided to postpone his education for a while.

For months on end he gave oats to the horses, hay to the cows, grain to the chickens, and slops to the pigs. He ended up adopting them all as his family. Every day he widened the circle of his relatives: a Charolais for a grandmother, a stallion for an uncle, a dirty pig for a cousin, and a flock of nephews and nieces squawking and squabbling in the barnyard for the choicest grain. But from the very beginning he dreamt of having a brother, a brother to whom he could whisper the worries that left him wet in his bed every night.

He missed not being able to trade hats or share a smoke with a brother. But he wouldn't have consented to call a calf or a colt his brother, not for all the gold in Peru. He just waited. He waited for he didn't know exactly who or what. . . . Then one day he found a dog.

He was a stray, that was certain, for Ti-Louis had found him crouched in the pig trough with the pigs grunting at him fit to burst. And from that day on Ti-Louis had a brother.

He is silent a moment. And the silence invades the fringes of the woods.

The dog died, its neck broken under the boot of the guard responsible for the welfare of the animals. Ti-Louis buried him high on a hill, under a willow, and the next night he left the State Farm by the back door, his boots strung round his neck and his knapsack stuffed with potatoes stolen from the pigs and corn from the chickens.

As he climbed the last fence he looked for the highway, but found only a sideroad and a few cow-paths. Where was the main road, then, the one that led to the centre of the globe? The great weathercock of the world spun so wildly over his head that its wings almost flew off, the winds blew contrariwise, and the wild geese, hesitant and perplexed, no longer knew which way to aim their beaks.

Suddenly his soul stretched, swelled, and began prickling his heart and the back of his neck, and Ti-Louis knew all he had to do was follow his nose. He knew that all nature would guide him, that the whole world would show him the way, that the land he sought had already nourished him for three or four centuries, and would not fail to recognize him as soon as he set foot on it.

His reserves of corn and small potatoes ran out at the Maine border, and for the past three days Ti-Louis has lived on hawthorn berries and green apples. The wind has died down during the night and the world seems to have been standing still since early this August morning. The weathercock has stopped spinning too, the trees are motionless, life is listening to itself breathe.

Now Ti-Louis hears his innards groaning. He looks around . . . not the hazelnut season yet . . . no beechnuts . . . not even acorns. . . . When a man's stomach is empty he easily takes yesterday's dreams for tomorrow's hopes, and Ti-Louis, rubbing his stomach with one hand, tries to rub his eyes open with the other — eyes full of sleep and sand and twitching from the itch of hunger and nine or ten nights under the Great Bear. Eyes he tries to train on a bunch of grotesque silhouettes dancing before him.

Under his palm he feels his eyelids chapped by lack of sleep. He forces his pupils open. Come on now! He may be starving, dead beat, out of breath, and short of energy, the oil in his joints may have turned to glue and his marrow may have hardened in his bones, but he's not crazy! At seventeen you don't lose your mind that easily! The spectacle unfolding before his eyes must be due to the evening sun . . . the seven o'clock sun playing hide-and-seek between the tamaracks and the birches, skipping from one branch to another, from one trunk to another, sowing grey and blue shadows in the furrows of the fields . . . it must be just the play of sunlight. . . .

"Holy Jesus and Mary! Has the sun got the cows dancing now?"

Ti-Louis the Whistler gives himself a kick in the pants and charges down on the herd of cows, chasing jays to their nests and jack-rabbits to their holes on the way. Then he stops within hailing distance, gasping for breath and blinking his eyes, and climbs up on a pile of fieldstones. There before him frolics a clan of merrymaking cows, simple barnyard animals, but bewitched and enraptured, drooling, staggering, cavorting, and sending a chorus of plaintive, cacophonous moos in his direction.

A sweet young Jersey freckled in rust from head to tail dips a bold horn towards him, rises on her hind legs, shakes her rump like a fledgeling ballerina, and turns on her public — him, the Whistler — a gentle, almond-shaped eye moist with joy and rapture. Ti-Louis would like to approach her, but at that moment the Jersey signals with her muzzle to one of her pals, a Guernsey who comes trotting over, rubs up against her, tickles her flank with the flat of her horn, and finally draws the two of them into a clumsy *pas de deux* which, amid quiverings and quaverings, suddenly lands them both on the ground like some splendid eight-limbed cactus.

Ti-Louis raises his eyes to heaven and calls on his father to restore his sanity, but his prayer is cut off by the waggle of a rump as a dowager cow serenely hoists her hoofs onto the shoulders of two of her calves who, one step to the right, one step to the left, draw their mother into a bovine ballet. This sight brings Ti-Louis back to his senses, for he now realizes he's not dreaming, not rambling, not dying; he is the sole privileged observer, on this summer evening early in August 1930, of a herd of cows on a spree. So swallowing his last apple with a hiccough, the young tramp from the south settles down on his pile of stones to see what comes next.

Well, if you'd only seen it! First a quadrille or *pas de quatre* with its ladies' chain, its change of partners, and its *swing your hoof right over the manger!* A big milker tries to clap her hoofs, but loses balance and pitches headfirst to the ground, leaving her vast, heart-shaped posterior smiling at the setting sun.

A heifer steps away from the clan, dusts off her white

robe with three swings of her tail, and climbs up on a haycock forgotten in the middle of the field. She stands there,
four feet clamped together as one, head stretched to the
sky, jaw hanging open, and wrings from her larynx such a
mooing plainchant that Ti-Louis is reminded of vespers in
the Irish church of his childhood. But the diva is too ambi-
tious; her uvula blocks on a note one higher than the top of
the scale, and she hangs there suspended between heaven
and earth with her jaws locked.

As Ti-Louis the Whistler rolls around on his pile of
rocks, clutching his sides, his hand suddenly discovers his
mouth-organ sewn into the lining of his coat. It is his only
family heirloom. A mouth-organ once borrowed, forgotten,
then left to him in lieu of heritage by a father who told him
on his deathbed:

"Play for the wise and the foolish alike, and if you run
out of notes, just stamp your foot."

That evening Ti-Louis the Musician plays for the cows
who, to thank him, change partners again: four steps forward, four steps back, a *branle*, a *tourné*, a *coupé*, a *vrille*,
rump rocking, eyes moist, dreaming, and half-closed.

. . . Mooo! . . . But what's got into him, the stupid thing?
A calf that's no longer a calf, a steer already, almost a little
bull, who thinks he can . . . oh! Look at him! You'd think
he'd never sucked a mother's udder, that one, with his barnyard manners. . . . Just look at him strutting around like a
little rooster! Oh, the scoundrel! Look at him running five
or six heifers at the same time, crowding them, tumbling
them, tickling and prodding them with his horns . . . hee
hee! As if that was the way for a cow to behave! You think
that's proper cowlike behaviour, such carryings-on?

The old black-and-white Holstein answers her milking mate by stiffening her tail to the vertical; then, her eye placid and glassy, she waters the roots of the mushrooms which spring up instantly in the amber spray.

A la claire fontaine plays the mouth-organ.

And the cow pisses all the stronger. They are all pissing abundantly tonight, as if they were under the sign of Niagara Falls. They piss, they twist, they giggle and reel, linking horns and nuzzling muzzles in a mooing madrigal, all drunk as a lord.

A short-lived orgy, *mesdames*, for with the rising of the full moon over the crest of the pines a little man, his eyes popping out of his head, comes running with huge strides across the field shouting at his dog to do something. His cows have gone mad! They're all completely mad, or drunk, for God's sake! The dog yaps and runs and nips the cows' shanks, and the cows trip and scamper trying to get away. What a hullabaloo! The calves hide under their mothers' bellies; the heifers give scandalized little moans; the steers brandish their nubs of horns, ready to charge as though they were in a corrida. . . . But what's got into them all? The convent Sisters' cowherd doubles and quadruples his efforts, fills the field with his "Co-boss! Co-boss!" and his flailing halter-rope, while his dog, stirred to a frenzy by all these carnival hijinks, thinks he'll soon be called in for the kill.

Ti-Louis the Whistler roars with laughter, slaps his thighs, and seeks the right rhythms on his harmonica to accompany this, the most glorious nocturnal jamboree ever presented as a spectacle to a seventeen-year-old vagabond newly returned to his native land.

Old Clovis had several narrow squeaks during the long August day and he was beginning to develop a taste for adventure.

This game of hide-and-seek with the bootleggers, the officers, and the villagers reminded him of his childhood. Besides, Clovis liked nothing better than a little fun. If he had listened to his heart, why. . . . But he told his heart to shut up, and his memories and imagination likewise . . . it was time to be serious. A store of delicious dreams lay waiting for him and his Companions of the Order of Good Cheer, all safely tucked away up there under the sod by the edge of the spring, well out of reach of any gravediggers, thieves, pilferers, or busybodies. Two barrelsful!

"Going to be a great winter!" Clovis told himself.

He made his way with a springy, rapid step to Maria's place. Little Eugène watched him open the gate without the least surprise. God had changed sides beginning that morning and the boy was ready for anything. So he accepted Clovis's peppermint as his just due and listened carefully to his instructions.

"Go tell Melchior the fisherman that Old Clovis is waiting for him and the others in the Sisters' cow-pasture. Now, repeat that to me."

Little Eugène rolled his peppermint under his tongue and repeated,

"Old Clovis is waiting for you and the others in the Sisters' pasture."

"The cow-pasture. Tell him to bring the others."

"Bring the others to the cow-pasture."

"Tell him to come quick."

"Come quick."

"Don't forget anything, Little-Next-to-Nothing. And tomorrow we'll have another ride in the wheelbarrow. The Sisters' cow-field, don't forget. Go on now!"

Eugène forgot neither the cows nor the Sisters. He

forgot Melchior. Crunching his peppermint, he went straight to Médard the fisherman, the one nicknamed Long-Tongue, and there delivered up Old Clovis's secret.

After Marie-Pet, Long-Tongue Médard was the most dangerous gossip on the coast. He fished neither lobster nor cod, for he suffered from seasickness. He fished for smelt, with rod and line, sitting on the dock. He didn't go out to sea, he went out to snoop. And this particular evening, without his even budging from his chair, gossip was coming to him. There he was rocking on his veranda this soft August evening, not hurting a fly, when smack into his lap, in the depths of his rocking-chair, fell the fattest bit of gossip of the season. He was completely flabbergasted.

"Old Clovis, you say?"

. . . Old Clovis who had so often made a fool of him, especially when mischief-making was afoot, like on Candlemas, or Mid-Lent, or Saint Valentine's Day. Old Clovis who never missed a chance to make him the laughing-stock of the whole countryside.

"He sent you to say he's waiting for me in the Sisters' field?"

"In the cow-pasture."

"The Sisters' cow-pasture!"

"He said to bring the others."

. . . The others? What others? Jacques, maybe, and Xavier-the-Hunchback?

Médard rocked his chair askew and narrowly missed the cat. It was the first time Old Clovis had ever deigned to summon him personally anywhere. And up with the convent cows, into the bargain!

"Did he say what time?"

Little Eugène had finished his candy and was wondering when Médard would start playing God-the-Good-Provider-and-Best-Friend-of-Little-Eugène with him . . . so he forgot to reply.

"Looks mighty fishy to me," said Médard between his teeth.

But for all that, he remained torn between curiosity and suspicion.

"Go tell your funny old friend Clovis the joker that Médard is too busy to go around chasing a bunch of cows."

But Little Eugène had worked out that the smelt fisherman wasn't one of his club, and was already galloping away over the sand dunes . . . Giddap there, Cayoose! . . . in anticipation of tomorrow's reward.

"I'm going over to smoke a pipe at Xavier's," said Médard to his wife, who wasn't listening.

But as soon as her man was out the gate Alisca ran through the back yard to her neighbour Régina's, who dragged her across to Marie-Louise's, who shoved them over to the Babineaus' to tell everything to Fat Emma.

The women held council: if the men thought they could just go off whenever they pleased to smoke their pipes in the Sisters' cow-pasture . . . well! They'd have to square that with their better halves first, that went without saying! Did anybody ever hear the like!

So while the smelt fisherman went over to Xavier-the-Hunchback's by way of the Babineaus' barn — "which just happened to be on the way" — and then by way of Gallant's stable and the general store, the wives ran, skirts hitched up, from Malvina to Jeanne to Célestine, who exclaimed in chorus,

"What! Behind the convent?"

"So they're up there taking a snort with the cows, are they?"

"You can count on me to bring my Xavier back by the ear; and if that doesn't do it. . . ."

But it would. Okay, Xavier, you can relax and uncross your legs now.

When the men reached the cow-field a little less than an hour later, a regiment of women armed with frying-pans and rolling-pins was waiting for them at the gate. And that's where the battle took place.

. . . Meanwhile, at their backs and unbeknownst to them, under a moon smiling from ear to ear, the Sisters' cowherd — stupefied and completely beside himself — was fighting desperately to bring his cows back to their senses. But the animals would not be tempted, either by sweet reason or by the comforts of the stable. The night was too inviting and the moon too wanton. They knew instinctively that such a gambol wouldn't come twice in one cow's lifetime, and that they'd better make the most of it. The old Holstein was the first to bite her partner's tail and drive her to break ranks.

Then all hell broke loose.

At which time the husbands and wives of Sainte-Marie-des-Côtes called a truce, at least long enough to look behind them, where they saw the real combat taking place out in the middle of the field. Well, not a combat — an exuberant Mardi Gras free-for-all.

The cows were bellowing up and down the scale, scampering here and there, shaking their big behinds under the noses of half the parish — all of whom had been sent to the Sisters' field by a little five-year-old snot-nose.

Then, like good hostesses, the cows led their guests to the spring . . . one barrel, two barrels, duly buried, unearthed by water rushing down the ruts and gullies formed by last night's storm, split open by a chance blow from a hoof, and now spreading out through the grass into a swamp of red wine and a stream of Napoleon brandy.

When Old Clovis and his friends finally tiptoed up the path leading to the cow-pasture, all Sainte-Marie-des-Côtes were already down on their knees around the barrels, lapping it up like gluttons.

The full moon was well up by the time Clovis managed to get back to the Three Kings, who were just starting their twentieth game of whist. He shook them up with kicks and punches, calling them a bunch of flabby-assed lazybones who didn't deserve the luck heaven had so generously handed them on a silver platter the day before.

"Bunch of degenerate slobs! That's what it is to have cards in your blood! The best Saint-Pierre and Miquelon have to offer cooling up there under the turf all this time, and . . . what are you playing, no trump?"

And he sends round a volley of cuffs and slaps.

"What the devil's going on, Clovis . . . ?"

Finally, in the midst of a storm of oaths, they managed to slip in a few questions about the real intentions of this guide and master of theirs, who had just disguised and hidden the biggest catch they'd made in all their years as sea-poachers. Old Clovis replied in broken, incomprehensible phrases, something about Little-Next-to-Nothing and the Sisters' pasture . . . and barrels in the cow-field . . . and how Clovis had spent three hours walking around the village, which was completely deserted . . . and how such calm and silence was a bad omen . . . and how someone was bound to catch on and come sniffing around at their cards for a whiff of the best-kept secret on the coast. . . .

Phew! At last he drew breath.

"I'm surprised at the little scamp," Old Clovis said to himself sadly as he led the three others to the foot of the convent hill.

"Better go round behind the barn," he warned prudently. "And not a sound, mind you. If you see the Sisters' hired man, sing *Partons, la mer est belle!*"

"Duck! There's some Sisters in the greenhouse!"

"Not a sound, now."

"Have I got time for a pee?"

But the vision that burst on the Three Kings as they rounded the barn and turned into the Sisters' field made them forget about peeing for quite some time.

The whole village had invaded the cow pasture — there they were, dancing, singing, sweet-talking each other, and swinging their partners to the strains of a harmonica juggled in the lips of a young stranger. Men and women shouting themselves hoarse, calling each other names, or enjoining friends and neighbours to quit worrying because the world was saved and the Depression over.

Clovis was first to catch on. Like a sledge-hammer blow to the brain, he got the message. Then he shook his grey locks, swallowed back a big gob of spit and:

"The devil is loose!" he exclaimed, giving Melchior a clap on the back that almost floored him. "Come on! Hurry up! Got to get up to the spring before it runs dry!"

Dieudonné raised his eyes to the too-bright night and tried to identify the shadows dancing beyond the convent. He knew already. The whole coast knew. He slowly choked back his anger and spite. And especially his shame. He had been made the plaything of a woman, one of the Crache-

à-Pic tribe! One of those sorcerers, outlaws, and misfits dragging out their existence on the fringe of the village by their
wits and what the sea washed up . . . nobodies . . . lawless,
godless, unprincipled creatures.

And the smuggler, who had built his own fortune out
of the ancestral lands of others and the illicit adventure of
rum-running, felt like throwing up on the Crache-à-Pics' dock.

But he resisted. It was his first big setback, and Dieudonné was wise enough to admit that fate had smiled on him
more often than not. The battle was lost but not the war.
The American president gone, mind you, and with him the
chance to make even his own family sit up and take notice,
accustomed though they were to turning a blind eye to his
new fortune.

"My father is in the lumber business," his sons would
declare gravely to their classmates at college.

And the classmates would snigger behind the backs of
the bootlegger's sons.

But Dieudonné could recoup. Higher than a president, in those days, reigned . . . Chicago's Al Capone.

"And this time no Crache-à-Pic will stand in my way,
even if I have to. . . ."

His wife didn't hear the end of his sentence, but she
saw her man's eye. And she was afraid.

At the very moment of this malediction Crache-à-Pic was
quietly landing at the dock her grandfather had built in front
of his house, at the foot of Cap-Lumière, fifty years before.
All day long the crew of the *Sea-Cow* had been joyfully stuffing themselves with lobster, lobster with that extra savour
of forbidden fruit.

So it was only on stepping ashore that the Galoshes

learnt of their bottles' stupendous odyssey. Crache-à-Pic consoled herself for their loss by thinking that through her — by way of three poachers, an old storyteller-longnosed-gossiping-busybody, and a snivelling little five-year-old bastard — the best wines and cognacs of Saint-Pierre, destined for the President of the United States, had gone down the gullets of a herd of cows.

And while Old Clovis and Ti-Louis the Whistler wobbled down from the field arm in arm, trying to pick out the forge from among the fifty-six dwellings of Sainte-Marie-des-Côtes, Crache-à-Pic burst out in that splendid, godlike laugh she'd inherited from an immemorial line of sailors and sorcerers.

CHAPTER TWO

OLD CLOVIS HAD AS MANY GRANDSONS AS ABRAHAM, NOT to mention his daughters and granddaughters. Yet he lived alone. In a shed his father had used as a blacksmith's shop. But Clovis-à-Clovis had about as much knack for blacksmithing as for French lace-making, so when his father died he turned the forge over to the rats and bats. He took possession again the day of the fourteenth childbirth under his roof, after his daughter-in-law Jeannette had spent the whole night moaning before bringing a cradleful of triplets into the world. That's enough now, he said. A man who lives on the coast doesn't fight the tides. So he moved his bed, his rocking-chair, and his frying-pan into his late father's forge.

From that day on Clovis was a new man. A new man?
... Hee-hee!

Clovis claimed on his deathbed that the days he spent in the forge were the best of his life. This blacksmith's son, though he didn't have an ounce of the smith in his veins, still had inherited the smells, the sounds, and the flickerings of flames and shadows that make the beams dance. That make images dance before your eyes, too, especially when you remember the vast repertoire of stories, tales, and sayings that trickled down to the village through the knotty planks of the forge. My father knew the forge well, knew Old Clovis, too . . . the things he could have told you . . . there was never a legend circulated freely in the land without first being sanctioned by the forge. Not a legend, nor a proverb, nor hearsay, nor fable, not a wisecrack or a scrap of gossip, nothing, not a word.

And because at the turn of the century people on the coast were more prone to gab than work, and better equipped to tell their life stories than to earn a living, Clovis-son-of-Clovis-the-blacksmith learnt the trade of storytelling from the forge, instead of blacksmithing.

Mind you, in this part of the world a storyteller is more than a spinner of tall tales, more than the inventor of *The Beast with Seven Heads* or *Saint Job Astride His Dungheap*. First and foremost a storyteller of Clovis's breed is a nose that quivers and an ear that perks up at any sound that's the least bit off key. As long as Marie-Pet jaws and jabbers away in *do-re-mi*, everything's okay, nothing out of the ordinary. But let her slide up the scale to *fa*, or worse, start blabbing in B-flat, why then. . . .

Ti-Louis the Whistler's ears are twitching. All this talk about off-key and B-flat in a deserted forge open to the four winds this August morning! The young harmonica player licks his chops. Does Old Clovis know something about music then? Would he maybe know how to read music?

Not on your life. Not the shade of a note. Not a hemi-demi-semiquaver. No, Old Clovis knows words, not notes. Knows them as well as the fleas in his shirt.

Ti-Louis the Whistler must have fallen asleep over the last pancake, for he woke this morning with raw gums and his teeth sticky with buckwheat flour.

"You've got the heavies," Old Clovis informed him. And thanks to this new word the youngster from the States learned that his bad dreams of the night before were not caused by hunger, as usual, but by pancakes floating in cognac and cow-field wine.

Little by little the two men recalled the previous night, complete with the party at the spring and the bovine caper under the full August moon. And a stereophonic peal of laughter filled the forge and woke up the flies, surprised at such a morning-after-the-night-before.

Last evening in the middle of the Sisters' field, Ti-Louis the Whistler had heard Clovis laugh even before he'd picked him out from the crowd. Collapsed between the two barrels down by the spring, he was laughing fit to burst. The youngster had come nearer, and little by little blended his own laughter with the old man's. Sparks and splashes of laughter over a range of two octaves. Then when the spring had dried up, the two laughers had looked each other in the eye, up, down, and all around, and shaken hands.

"What name does a ghost like you go by, and where does he hail from?"

"From the States, and Ti-Louis the Whistler's my nickname."

People of the coast were too used to nicknames to give a second thought to one like this. But from the States, now, that gave pause. During the Depression a tramp showing bare toes in front and a bare ass behind might have come from Bedèque or Caraquet, or even from Québec for that matter . . . but from the United States of America?

"In the States they've got skyscrapers; here, we're pot-scrapers," the old pot-licker laughed.

Ti-Louis started to join in but a cramp seized his stomach. And while he looked for a way to tell Old Clovis that he hadn't put a thing in his gut for the last three days, he heard,

"Have you eaten yet?"

So while the village continued the carnival of cows and Napoleon brandy until late into the night, under the horrified eyes of the Sisters watching this witches' sabbath from every window in the convent, Ti-Louis followed Old Clovis to the forge.

And next day, when his stomach had settled and his ears were filled with the buzzing of flies stroking their wings in the pool of sunlight, the ghost from the States listened to old storyteller Clovis recount the ways of the coast.

"You've no idea the kind of country you've come to," said he.

... A fine country it was all the same, and one that might let you believe in a peaceful, respectable future lying hidden somewhere along the coast, between the forest and the sea. And why not, after all! It was young and unspoiled, and well served by four distinct seasons that never trod on each others' heels. Ah no! You don't find spring showing up early in a land like this, you can be sure of that! It was a country whose people were beginning to develop a taste for life, by God! a rage, an itch to live! You know what it is to have the itch? Everybody on the coast was ready to believe the first shyster to come along and promise them a patch of land to plant their cabbages on. It reached the point where hucksters and hoaxters and sellers of rain-machines were a dime a dozen. No sooner had a stranger hitched his horse in the main street than the whole village rushed over to hear about the new railroad, or the Papal zouaves, or the Alaska gold rush. And when a schooner tied up at the dock — *ooh, la-la!*

In those days they'd have believed a sailor counting up his castles in Spain as easily as a fisherman toting up his lobster-pots.

"And then one day the genuine article stepped ashore,

one who singlehanded could have taken the whole region's coat and turned it inside out on the spot, or even reversed the tides. No lie! This fellow could have jumped up and caught the moon in his teeth."

There it was, then. That day an authentic giant of a sorcerer landed at Sainte-Marie-des-Côtes. And don't anyone go raising an eyebrow, either! If there's a country that knows real giants and sorcery when it sees them, why. . . .

"And he called himself Crache-à-Pic. Call him Spit-in-Your Eye, Spit-Fire, or Spit-Plumb-on-Target — he was a wonder!"

A strapping seven feet tall he was — according to Clovis's yardstick — all decked out in muscles and moustaches, with hair in his nose, a real Gaulois chief. The first time he crossed the village, even the *curé* greeted him. Bowed low, too low, a bad sign. A parish can have only one cock stuck up on its steeple.

The battle was long and hard since the combatants were of equal strength. Each met his match, but only after they had surprised and surpassed themselves with remarkable feats of supernatural power, the *curé* grappling with all his might to exorcize the bewitched, the sorcerer giving him good measure and instructing Christians in the catechism of Albertus Magnus.

This giant of a man was the father of the Cap-Lumière lobster fisherman who disappeared at sea one day leaving a widow with three or four kids in short pants . . . no, one of the kids was a girl, now captain of the *Sea-Cow*. Furthermore, the son followed close on the father's heels, right into the grave.

"In a manner of speaking, of course. On account of because neither of them had the right to a real grave. The

son because he was lost at sea, and the old man because. . . .
How old are you, anyway?"

Ti-Louis sits up with a jerk. He's seventeen . . . and so
what? He's old enough to hear and understand anything.
Especially after what he's lived through in the past two years.
. . . Tsk! Tsk! The old storyteller shakes his head. Nobody's
lived through enough, not even Old Clovis himself, to hear
the rest of the story without a shudder. And he casts a crit-
ical eye at the flies playing with fire around a spider web,
then signals them to keep quiet. It's a time for gravity.

Crache-à-Pic Senior, with his handlebar moustache and
his hairy nose, was a tough old nut. And a prankster.

"He really liked to play tricks."

For example, he liked to make the punishment fit the
crime. That's how he came to make a boil grow on the
thigh of the wife of . . . well, never mind; and bewitched the
biggest miser in Cocagne so he went out one fine morning
and planted his money in the furrows along with the wheat;
and gave a dose of the clap to the biggest prude on the
coast; and cast a spell on none other than Marie-Pet's own
mother so that right in the middle of the *Offertory*, to the
great delight of the whole parish, she sounded off with *O
My Darling Clementine*.

But that was the limit. The Church could put up with
attacks on animals, crops, or even its own parishioners. But
not on God. And that very day the *curé* of Sainte-Marie-des-
Côtes. . . .

Old Clovis made the sign of the cross.

"That day the *curé* of Sainte-Marie-des-Côtes had had
it. Right up to here."

He decided to take his revenge. Sorcerer Crache-à-Pic
had attacked the Church, eh? Well, the Church was going

to attack him right back. So on Sunday morning, in full pomp, with its biretta on its head and its golden chasuble right down to its ankles, from the heights of the pulpit the Church condemned this so-called Crache-à-Pic, who for want of a proper Christian name had to settle for a nickname. From that moment on the *curé* forbid any of his parishioners to have woman, child, or animal treated by that notorious charlatan, under pain of being denied the sacraments. And the whole sentence couched in the purest Church Latin.

"The poor priest should have kept his trap shut," Clovis concluded, "and not let sorcery in through that particular hatch."

Even after so many years, the old storyteller still laughed at the memory of the raging toothache that descended upon the *curé* that Sunday right after the *Ite missa est.*

Two weeks of prayers, fasting, and promises to all the saints, plus daily visits to healers, midwives, doctors, and tooth-pullers, had no effect on the abscess. The best-known remedies, both natural and supernatural, remained powerless. Not a thing could be done. Meanwhile the poor victim was failing fast. The parish, which had laughed at first, began to worry.

There was only one solution. But nobody dared mention it. Such things are too delicate. For that matter, even after the event nobody dared affirm that the priest had actually tried it. Not even that terrible old centenarian, Ozite the Chronicler, who the day of her hundredth birthday began to mock everything as though the future held no fears for her. No, nobody in the country dared suggest for certain that the priest. . . . They simply let the evidence speak for itself, sure that there at least you couldn't go wrong: the sudden, total, miraculous cure of the toothache, followed by the reconciliation of the two enemies. Period. That's all. Not a word more. Of course Marie-Pet's mother tried to . . . but they silenced her. The priest was cured, the two miracle workers reconciled. The battle of the giants was not to be. So you can all go home.

So there!

The battle did take place, however — but beyond the tomb.

In the secret recesses of his soul the *curé* had surely harboured a serpent's tooth of resentment against the sorcerer. For many years later, at the death of Crache-à-Pic, the Church refused this "pagan and unbeliever" a Christian burial. There was family outcry, some neighbours protested, and finally the priest found this expedient: to calm the anger of his flock a hardwood log was substituted, by night, for the cadaver of the sorcerer, and this was buried in the Christian cemetery; while to appease the anger of the gods, the true corpse of the miscreant was buried in a grave under an apple tree in his own back yard.

So that's how order was finally restored. An eye for an eye and a tooth for a tooth. Along the coast, the era of sorcery ended with the first of the great Crache-à-Pics. And the Church rubbed its hands in glee . . . but the rubbing developed calluses. . . .

One year to the day after this watered-down funeral, Crache-à-Pic the sorcerer remembered that he had not been properly laid to rest, and decided to wake up again.

"That very morning a ball of fire as big as a dog burst up from under the apple tree in the Crache-à-Pics' back yard, spun around like a top, faster and faster, bigger and bigger, throwing off flames to right and left, then set off through the village on the north side of the King's Highway, knocking down houses, barns, and sheds on its way, till it reached the church. And there it threw a glove of fire round the steeple and tossed it into the sea, and nobody's ever been able to fish it up since."

They even say that besides the parish steeple this tornado, ever after called "sorcerer Crache-à-Pic's hurricane", also whirled away the famous *curé*'s biretta, one of his slippers, and his set of china clippers.

A tooth for a tooth.

This hurricane then . . . big as a dog and spinning like a top . . . carried the whole north half of the village away in a whirlwind of fire, ripping off roofs and dormers, knocking down verandas, striking cracks into walls, and shivering timbers. It was the worst catastrophe the coast had ever known, including the big fire at Miramichi, and much bigger than Halley's Comet a few years later. And do you want to know something else? This same catastrophe was the start of big Dieudonné's fortune.

In those days at the turn of the century he was a lone wolf, and a hungry one, roaming the sand dunes in search of prey and adventure. He sniffed like a weasel, spied like a fox, and ranged like a wolf, sure that sooner or later the prize would fall from the tree right at his feet. Luck belongs to him who can wait the longest. One day fortune would smile on him in an unexpected and singular way, he was sure of it.

And fortune, in the guise of the tornado, did indeed give Dieudonné the chance to enrich himself from the ruins of his country.

Sainte-Marie-des-Côtes, together with the neighbouring villages to north and south, occupied a stretch of land squeezed in between the forest and the sea. Water and trees

— his fortune would spring from one or the other. And letting his eyes roam over the sheds and buildings battered by the hurricane, young Dieudonné decided it would be the trees.

At that time, to encourage the clearing of those inexhaustible forests that covered the coast, the government was distributing parcels of land in standing timber to all and sundry. Dieudonné obtained first one concession, then another registered in the name of a brother, then one for a cousin, an aunt, or a son-on-the-way, and so on right down to a relative of the fifth degree who had been dead for a good fifteen years. It was a time when the government in Fredericton hadn't yet learnt to pronounce such barbarous French names as Thibodeau, Goguen, Bordage, Mazerolle, Girouard, or Gautreau. The old civil service clerk, whose own name was John Jonathan Featherstonehaugh, had never in the whole of his long career learnt to tell a Comeau from a Cormier, or a Robidoux from a Robichaud. And Dieudonné, who was descended by hip and thigh from all these different branches, succeeded in clearing over to himself half the forest bordering his home turf.

To the general amusement of friends and neighbours.

But the laughter turned sour when they woke up one day to find their foreheads pressed against "No Trespassing" signs put up by the new master of the coast.

"What's going on?"

"Is everybody going to end up in Dieudonné's hip pocket?"

The people of the coast like nothing better than to thumb their noses at government, the English, or any other boss. And they heartily applaud any character craftier than the one before. Until the day the trickster begins cashing in on his trick, and becomes master in turn — at which point they set out to shortchange the shortchanger. Dieudonné, who had been born on the coast, knew the mentality of his fellow countrymen like the back of his hand. So he set things up for himself.

"To the woods, men! Jobs for everyone! I'm paying the shot!"

That changed everything. Dieudonné was paying. Hey, Xavier-the-Hunchback! Hey, fisherman of the Village-des-Trois-Maisons! To the woods! Come on, men! A forest of walnut, maple, fir, and spruce ready for the axe.

And Dieudonné was paying; or promised to pay as soon as he began to turn a profit. . . . A profit? What profit? Shut up and chop. Dieudonné knows what he's doing and he knows a good deal when he sees one.

Doesn't he just, though!

So everyone chopped. A bunch of carpenters' sons were even hired to build a sawmill on Dieudonné's land. A thoroughly respectable sawmill that one Monday morning started turning those oaks, pines, maples, firs, walnuts, mountain ash, and poplars into fine straight planks.

Then one day Clovis, the blacksmith's son, dared scratch an ear and mutter,

"Just what's Dieudonné thinking of doing with all those planks, then?"

And his father replied, scratching the back of his neck,

"If you want my opinion, he's thinking of selling them back to us to rebuild our sheds and buildings."

As Clovis-son-of-Clovis had to admit later, his father had judged right. In his first big operation Dieudonné proved himself to be the greatest capitalist in the east of the country. He rebuilt the village with planks from his mill made from trees cut on Crown lands . . . cut by the sweat of the brows of friends and countrymen who paid for the planks with the same money Dieudonné owed them in wages for having cut down his trees which they themselves had dragged to the mill and sawed into planks to build their houses with. . . . Phew! What a genius the man was!

And a generation later, Old Clovis mops his brow in admiration.

While the storyteller was telling Ti-Louis from the States the Dieudonné chapter in the chronicles of the coast, this same Dieudonné, hardened by thirty years of trade and ten of smuggling, was peering at the horizon beyond the dunes where the Crache-à-Pics' dock lay hidden. She wanted to see some action, did she? Was looking for a little adventure? Dieudonné swore to himself that he'd keep her occupied. . . . He'd provide her distraction, he'd send her out on false scents and down blind alleys, give her her fill of fireworks and fantasies, shackle her wrists to the rain-machine.

So one day. . . .

"Philias, go get me Black Willy."

Dieudonné had just discovered the perfect way to keep those pillaging lobster-poachers and that young bitch of a Crache-à-Pic tied to the same stake. The bootlegger needed a free hand; he had to control the King's Highway, and several sideroads as well, so his trucks could roll freely right over to the American border by night. And time was running short. But he'd worked it out. Two birds with one stone!

And Zéphirine, without the twitch of an eyebrow or the trace of a limp, watched her master go off to the barn where his secret telegraph lay hidden.

That August, Sainte-Marie-des-Côtes didn't just settle for a carnival in the cow-field. Oh no! It also treated itself to a fantastic giant bazaar for the poor. They called it Marie-Pet's picnic. It was a real parish picnic, done up brown according to all the rules, far bigger and better than those puny little picnickettes given by Cocagne, Grand-Digue, or Pré-d'en-Haut. Somebody had been trying to put one over on Marie-Pet, eh? Well, Marie-Pet was going to send that somebody right back to get their nose wiped in their mother's skirts. And as for a picnic — she had a picnic all right!

Aside from Clovis, nobody in Sainte-Marie-des-Côtes guessed the origin of the parish-wide commotion that mobilized the *curé*, his servant, the League of the Sacred Heart, and the whole convent and sent every do-gooding patroness of the parish down to the church basement cooking up chicken stew. A bazaar with proceeds to the poor right in the middle of the Depression, think of it!

And Old Clovis laughed into his salt-and-pepper beard.

"Nobody will ever know that Sainte-Marie-des-Côtes's picnic was conceived in a wheelbarrow," he confided to the flies and spiders of the forge. And then, thinking of his new friend Ti-Louis the Whistler, he added,

"Was conceived for the express purpose of giving that frisky young newcomer from the States a chance to show us up here just what he could do."

And the newcomer had shown them that he could warble and stomp his foot and let his hair down and go on playing his mouth-organ long after the last violinist or Jew's harp player had dropped from exhaustion headfirst into the bran barrel. For a parish bazaar is, above all . . .

. . . chicken stew and lobster and dumplings and apple fritters and music!

... boxing, wrestling, hammer-throw, pole-vault, shooting-matches, tug-of-war, and music!

... firecrackers, balloons, flags, garlands, posters, fireworks, and music!

... lotteries, bingo, storytelling, doorprizes, fortune's wheel, and music!

... polkas, quadrilles, jigs, waltzes, gavottes, *swing your boot right into the wood-box*, and music!

A regular musical merry-go-round!

Marie-Pet was overwhelmed. She had wanted this picnic to restock the parish coffers, and put the noses of the doctor's wife and the priest's servant out of joint for having thought they could do without her services. But she had just wanted a picnic, not Sodom and Gomorrah! The devil had cut loose at the sound of the violin, the Jew's harp, the guitar, the accordion, the bagpipes, the hurdy-gurdy, and the mouth-organ. A parade of musicians who played themselves silly for three days and two nights. For by the third night the parish couldn't muster a single mouth or right hand capable of striking a chord or blowing a note. It was then that Ti-Louis the Whistler had his chance.

He played the harmonica all night long, building new rhythms from old melodies, grimacing, twisting, tapping his foot, waving his limbs around like a scarecrow in the breeze. And getting its second wind, the parish gathered itself up and set to dancing again. By the time morning came around everyone knew that he'd come from the States, that he was called Ti-Louis the Whistler, and that he was the son of Charles-à-Charlitte from the Grelot branch who had left to make his fortune in the paper mills of Massachusetts.

"I hear tell your father died of hunger?"

"No, consumption."

75

"Same thing."

So that day Sainte-Marie-des-Côtes welcomed Ti-Louis the Whistler in as one of their own.

"You don't have any relations around here?"

He had an aunt. One of his father's sisters had stayed on the coast and remarried, some guy from the north. She had a gold tooth and was called Célestine.

Old Clovis chuckled. He knew only one gold tooth in the village, and it wasn't lodged in Célestine's jaw but dangled from the upper gum of Dieudonné's wife.

"Your guy from the north must have sold his wife's tooth for a mug of beer!"

And taking Ti-Louis by the arm, he led him off to meet Célestine.

"I'm bringing you your nephew," said he on the doorstep. "He's fresh up from the States."

Ti-Louis the Whistler waited for her to speak or smile so he could check out the gold tooth. But Célestine just stood there, arms hanging, a gentle but worried look on her face. Three little ragamuffins lined up against the wall stole suspicious glances at this stranger eyeing their soup bowls. Finally Célestine extended a hand chapped from laundry work and chucked her young nephew under the chin. He smiled at the caress.

"So you buried your father," she said.

No gold tooth.

"Two years ago."

"That so? Well, step in."

Clovis excused himself; he had urgent work to do. His smithy-home smelt of soot and was sagging under a coat of dust woven thicker than spider webs. No lie. Once a season, whether it needed it or not, he took a broom to it,

wielding his weapon as a knight does his sword. A fine carn-
age there'd be that morning. Let intruders beware!

"It's August fifteenth, Clovis — Assumption," said Célestine, smiling for the first time.

"Well now, you don't say so!" said the old man, easily
changing tack. "In that case I'll be going over to the church
to dust off a pew with the seat of my pants."

And off he went, saying with his eyes to his young
friend: There now, my boy, you've got some relatives up
here after all.

But as he pushed the gate closed behind him he saw
the guy from the north, Célestine's husband, slobbering and
reeling, apparently coming home from the Babineaus' barn.
Old Clovis gave him the local greeting, calling out, "Take
care now," as the custom is. But customs in the north differ
from those in the south, and the drunkard took the greeting as an insult.

"Take care yourself, or I'll break your jaw, you son of
a bitch," he spat at Clovis, threatening him with his fist.

And Old Clovis, forgetting his mass of the Assumption of the Virgin Mary and heading home to his forge,
thought wistfully about the poor little lad from the States.

During the first half of the autumn the two friends
saw each other often — the country is so small — in the
hollows of the dunes, on the docks, by the bluffs, or simply
in the forge. And each of them avoided the subject of Aunt
Célestine and her boozing husband. Clovis would content
himself with offering Ti-Louis an apple — Go ahead, take
two — buckwheat pancakes with molasses from Agnès's kitchen, or leftover baked beans heated up from the night
before.

It was one such evening, just at dusk, that Ti-Louis the

Whistler and Clovis, caught with their mouths full of beans, saw the door of the forge kicked open to make room for three wild-eyed kings who all seemed to want in at the same time.

"Clovis! Old Crache-à-Pic's come back!"

Clovis spits out his beans and clutches his stomach. Not so fast there, not so fast, calm down and don't all talk at once. Exactly who and what and where and how . . . and take your time, weigh your words, use short, simple, sensible sentences and. . . .

"What!?!"

The Three Kings repeat their sentence in all its clarity and sim-pli-ci-ty: Old Crache-à-Pic has come back!

. . . The Old Man? You mean the grandfather? The one with the hurricane . . . ?

"The one that was buried under the apple tree in the back of his house?"

The very one. Snuck back like a spook. Stripped down to the bones. He's already appeared to three kids coming home from picking hazelnuts, to Xavier-the-Hunchback quietly leading his team down to the shore for a load of seaweed, and to Old Cyprien's daughter-in-law by her first marriage, Célestine by name.

Ti-Louis the Whistler sits bolt upright. A ghost! A real ghost right over at his place!

No, no. Not over at Célestine's. So far he's only appeared in one single place, at the end of Lovers' Lane where it meets the King's Highway. And after sunset.

Clovis screws up his eyes.

"In his bare bones, you say, and at sunset? So how come you know it's Old Crache-à-Pic?"

Melchior mumbles, blinks both eyes, then shuts up. But Gaspard and Balthazar make no bones about it. Since

when do you ask a ghost for his passport? Isn't it enough
that Célestine and Xavier and the children recognized him?

. . . The children?

Clovis reflects that the sorcerer has been dead for a
quarter of a century . . . but he keeps his reflections to himself, and decides to follow the three poachers up to Lovers'
Lane.

It's Hallowe'en.

There's already a teeming crowd at the foot of the
road. The curious have assembled there from the south, the
north, and the back country. From the dunes and hills around
the two-century-old oak that separates Lovers' Lane from
the King's Highway, cartloads of Hallowe'en celebrants have
already gathered, all dressed up in their costumes, ghost or
no. Of course, an honest-to-goodness ghost does give Hallowe'en quite a different flavour.

"Put your jack-o-lanterns out, boys. Make room for
the dead."

"If all the villages round and about keep sending over
more folks, there soon won't be room for the living."

"Well, if there's any one of the living don't feel at home
here, all he's got to do is play dead to get a little respect."

"Don't laugh at death, Melchior. Remember, one day
you'll end up dead too."

"You really think so? Well, in that case I'd better get
my laughing in while there's still time!"

The crowd roars with mirth, coos with pleasure, tosses
off friendly gibes, and forgets the dead. The funmakers are
so full of beans that even the girls from up the hill are having trouble pretending to be afraid. Anyway, tonight death
is disguised as Crache-à-Pic. . . .

"Is it really Old Crache-à-Pic, then?"

"We'll know for sure when we lay hold of him!"

Ho-ho! Lay hold of a ghost? To begin with, there's nothing to lay hold of. A ghost is kind of white floating stuff, like a dead soul, sort of shapeless, a bunch of cotton wool with neither head nor tail, a thing you can't grab.

Poor Crache-à-Pic! So he's got neither head nor tail now! Isn't that a caution! And all the men begin to commiserate with him.

At that Old Clovis leaves the site of the apparition, scattering a flock of urchins hanging onto his cape and tangling in his legs, and clucking, tsk! tsk! tsk! A phantom at the end of Lovers' Lane on a night of full moon? Come on now, phantoms are as afraid of the moon as they are of their own shadows, everyone knows that.

"But it's Hallowe'en, Clovis. Anything can happen then."

Just so. Hallowe'en's a night for tricks. It's not the Day of the Dead. Célestine and the Hunchback were seeing things, and the kids invented the rest.

"Go play your tricks somewhere else."

But shuffle their feet as they may, twist their shoulders north or south or towards the hills, they still keep their eyes riveted on the skeletal branches of the oak where a ghost from beyond the grave floated just last night.

"Go on back home," Clovis insists.

"Okay, okay, let's go," the crowd mutters.

They start to move but they are pushed back against the oak by a new wave of rubberneckers come down from the hills, who are pushed in turn by a crowd coming from the woods.

"What's going on, anyway?"

The newcomers claim their part of the vision, for in

this country of patronage and privilege it's always the same ones who get everything. The coast had the right to its carnival of cows, and its game of hide-and-seek with the bootleggers, and now heaven itself goes and sends them a genuine ghost. It's too much for one village. The back country is determined to share this ghost with them, if they have to take him hostage to do it.

Suddenly the crowd closes, sways, then parts in the middle . . .

"Hey! Quit pushing!"

. . . and lets through Martial, the representative of the law. Célestine and Xavier-the-Hunchback step forward as eye-witnesses of the first water; then relatives, neighbours, and fellow-fishermen, the curious, the cousins of the curious, the cousins three and four times removed, the whole shoving, elbowing crowd — watch out, that fellow's horning in there — the whole lot of them, arms and legs locked, surround the constable. Lucky for him that just at this moment reinforcements arrive from town, in the persons of a sheriff and two fisheries officers.

Decidedly, all the representatives of the law are on deck tonight, thinks Clovis. Not a one missing. Hmmm! And out loud for the benefit of Ti-Louis, the young sprout from the States:

"Can't think of a single self-respecting ghost would put in an appearance with all that government brass hanging around," he says.

No, eh? The ghost must have heard this and taken it as a challenge.

. . . .

A collective "Aaaah!" rises from the roots of the oak, is echoed from mouth to mouth, and spreads out in widening circles till at the farthest range it reaches the ears of Clovis and Ti-Louis the Whistler.

"Sweet Jesus Son of Mary!"

The crowd is staggered. The timorous have their backs to the oak while the bold ones face the apparition; this criss-cross pattern heightens the panic, which explodes in a burst of magnificent terror.

There he is, naked right down to his backbone, danc-ing above their heads at the junction of the King's Highway and Lovers' Lane. A skull and a skeleton white as chalk, with long gangling legs swaying like branches in a nor'eas-ter, freshly unearthed, stripped to the marrow, washed clean as a whistle right down to the teeth . . . teeth that are grin-ning, grimacing, grinding, getting ready to bite!

"Woo-oo-oo!"

He's groaning, calling, trying to say something. . . . Let's get out of here! . . . No, listen to what he has to say. . . . Get out of my road, Jacques! . . . Shh! Shut up! . . . Watch out, he's coming right down on the crowd! Aiee! Aiee! Mamma! . . . Quiet, be quiet. . . . Make room for him there. . . .

As curious-looking a phantom as ever you saw. . . . To tell the truth, nobody ever saw one before, of any kind. It's hard to compare, but he must be like the others. Except that this one really looks as if he's out for a good time, wants to get some fun out of life . . . as if it didn't bother him a scrap to be dead, as though he felt quite at home in his bones.

. . . Just look at him now! Seems to want to get up close to that bunch of young girls shoved in under the wil-low tree. Just like Crache-à-Pic, that. Now there's a dead man hasn't forgotten much about life! He's shaking his neck and his arms, stretching out a forearm with six or seven finger joints dangling in space. . . . Hey! Don't let him do that! He could cast a spell on them. A dead man touching the living transmits the germ of death. . . . But don't you go worrying about those girls from the coast; they're too used to fishermen and sailors to be caught unawares by any skeleton. And like a flock of birds surprised in their nest they scatter into the bushes.

Disappointed, the phantom turns off, disappears, takes off, nothing left. A puff of wind has blown him out like a candle. A horrible vacuum invades the place, and nobody dares think or breathe. But there he is, popping up over by the pine grove; went right across the King's Highway and there he is again, as lively as ever. Ti-Louis the Whistler, who has been getting used to the strange customs of the coast since the cow carnival, gets close and reaches out his hand, but the ghost sees him coming and disappears in a whirlwind again.

Ahh! Too bad. And just when he was beginning to get used to us and let himself be tamed down a little. Who's the dummy went and frightened him?

Ti-Louis ducks down and melts into the crowd.

Now everyone starts to realize that the spectre won't return tonight. Marie-Pet can go back to her prayers, and the others back to wherever they came from.

"You'd all better go home," says Constable Martial, trying to recover from his emotions. "I'll spend the rest of the night looking around, with the other officers."

"It's Hallowe'en," risks Xavier-the-Hunchback.

The night for tricks, thinks Old Clovis.

And Ti-Louis the Whistler — who in the past three months has seen cows dance and a ghost gambol — looks up to heaven to see if the sky is likely to come falling down.

The folks from the back country finally leave, dragging their feet and swearing they'll be back tomorrow.

"Tomorrow's All Saints' Day," Clovis reminds them.

His remark doesn't seem to mean much to the frisky younger generation, who are not well enough versed in sorcerers' ways to see that, logically, somebody like Crache-à-Pic should refrain from appearing on a day set aside to commemorate the saints. But if it doesn't ring a bell with the youngsters, Clovis's observation does strike Black Willy's ear like a gong as he slinks around in the crowd thinking himself incognito. So incognito that everyone carefully steps on his toes hoping to hear him yelp or swear; so incognito that Old Clovis fixes him with a stare without seeming to and then, turning his back on Dieudonné's man, repeats as if to himself, "Crache-à-Pic, if those bones be his, will never appear on All Saints' Day."

And on All Saints' Day the ghost stayed home.

The crowd of inquisitive spectators came next day just the same, from Cocagne, Champdoré, and Village-des-Trois-Maisons, and waited there all night long.

. . . It's not fair! half of them said.

. . . It's a trick! said the other half.

. . . Could it be he's moved off somewhere else? wondered those from Pré-d'en-Haut, who had come by truck to be at the foot of Lovers' Lane by dusk.

Pré-d'en-Haut might grumble and Cocagne complain all they liked; the dead man stayed with the dead on All Saints' Night.

Old Clovis chuckles.

"I said as much. I told you that ghost wouldn't be back on All Saints'."

But Clovis is careful not to reveal the reason he said so. His prediction was aimed over the ghost's head at the incognito Black Willy, and thus at Dieudonné. And the bootleggers, though they pass for sly foxes, have taken the bait. Old Clovis slaps his thigh. Then, leaning towards his protégé from the States, drops into his ear:

"There are forty-six ways to trap a bear, but the best way's to make him think he's a fox."

Apprentice Ti-Louis looks at his master and blinks in amazement. The adventure of rum-running is opening up to him, in all its seductive detail, as an epic of contraband evolving in a series of tricks and pranks played out between clowns and sharpers. And at the centre of this multiple farce is an old, weasel-nosed, inquisitive magician who with a crack of his whip can set things going at the speed of a galloping horse.

. . . The contraband network of the twenties was as intricate as a thickset oak, and cast a shadow the size of the continent. One of its branches, a main one endowed with impressive foliage, covered the east coast. Between the brains of the organization in Chicago and the chief furnishers, the French islands of Saint-Pierre and Miquelon, stretched a string of villages forgotten by explorers and map-makers alike but serving as relays in the great bootlegging network. And proudly standing head and shoulders above them all was the village of Sainte-Marie-des-Côtes.

"And Sainte-Marie-des-Côtes was Dieudonné."

In the year 1928 he thought he saw his star falter. One fine day this man — who'd spent six years mounting his organization and then extending it across the three maritime provinces, and little by little even nibbling away at Quebec — saw the government of Canada, calmly and without advance warning, declare an end to Prohibition. Just like that, without consultation or public opinion polls, acting entirely on its own say-so, the government went and abolished a law that had done more for the country's economy than all the job-creation and social-welfare programs put together. And right on the eve of the greatest economic crisis the world had ever seen. Dieudonné couldn't get over it.

The repeal of the law prohibiting the sale of alcohol spelt death to the contraband trade and an end to the bootleggers. Sure enough, one after another the small dealers hung up their jugs and closed shop. Government liquor stores operating in the open replaced the clandestine trade in barns, cellars, and fish sheds.

The small bootleggers were short on nerve and imagination, though, as Old Clovis remembered. They should have known human nature better, and remembered the taste of stolen apples. Dieudonné did. He understood fully that government outlets operating in broad daylight would never rival nocturnal business done in a barn between two bales of hay.

Then one day, he had his great idea: the States! Although Prohibition had ended on Canadian soil, it still continued in the U.S.A. And the frontier between the two countries, then as now, stretched in one continuous line from Atlantic to Pacific. Hundreds of customs points linked Canada to its one and only neighbour, plus thousands of clandestine passages: forest paths, portages, lakes, rivers, sideroads, open fields, railway lines, pastures, mountain passes, and the sea.

The sea! What a prodigious link that was!

. . . Old Clovis licks his chops.

From 1928 on the sea was covered with hulls and sails, and throbbed to the roar of Chrysler and Bessamer motors.

Ships as long as one hundred and twenty feet could carry a cargo of forty-eight tons, up to twelve hundred cases of bottles, to be delivered to some Caribbean free port or, more likely, exchanged for hard cash right at sea. The risks were enormous: risk of storm, risk of seizure in port or within territorial waters, risk of armed combat between the cutters of the Crown and the bootleggers' Scottish Fisherman boats.

Old Clovis and his peers watched this comic war with high amusement but remained neutral, as common folk always do before a clash of princes, content to applaud whichever of the contestants showed himself more skilful, quick, or sly. Clovis laughed to himself at the memory of the barbarous names the bootleggers gave their boats with the sole aim of baffling the customs men, who could never distinguish between the *Tatamagouche*, the *Mistouche*, the *Malagache*, the *Madagouiac*, or the *Kouchibougouac*. So it was the innocent *Fanny May* who got picked up more often than she deserved.

This maritime chase had been going on for two years when Dieudonné planned and brought off his first big coup by land. His province was a godsend, made to measure for rum-runners in Prohibition days. A ragged rectangle with Maine on its back and Québec's Gaspésie on its shoulders, it booted Nova Scotia with its right foot and Cape Breton with its left, and all the rest lay wide open to the winds of the Atlantic. It was a real nest for adventurers, and they made good use of it.

One of these, Polyte Lévesque by name, reigned over a kingdom as vast as Dieudonné's and had accustomed the three or four counties to the north to be ready for anything:

to see small airplanes appear from nowhere, land in the middle of their potato fields, and then take off almost immediately for some unknown destination; to see five or six trucks running without lights sweep down out of the night in perfect silence; to see far more hearses and ambulances passing on the King's Highway than there were dead or dying in the land.

"One day," Old Clovis relates, "they say Polyte offered the *curé* of his parish a whole load of bricks to finish building his church. A whole boxcar full of them which the *curé* rushed down to the station to pick up. Hee-hee! A boxcar filled with a wall of bricks on the outside, but inside filled with bottles of rum which our fine friend Polyte unloaded into his barn during the night. Hee-hee-hee! The church of Saint Whatchamacallit of Madawaska still isn't finished yet, from what I hear."

And at the memory of this anecdote Old Clovis's eyes moisten with pleasure and emotion.

But Polyte's finest triumph, one that won even Dieudonné's admiration and spurred him on in the trade, was the bishop's procession. It happened during confirmation time. The local pastor, like bishops the whole world over, did the rounds of his diocese every four years to apply three drops of holy chrism to the foreheads of those who had been baptized before and had now reached the age of reason. It was a chance for the parishes to march out in procession to meet their pastor, resplendent in his golden *magna capa* and his bishop's mitre pointing up to heaven like a church steeple. And for the bishop to bless his flock with his golden crosier sparkling with jewels.

In the spring of 1929 word got out that the bishop would be making his rounds a year earlier than usual. No problem, really, it was just that this time he was going to confirm a bunch of little Christians on the American side of the border. So all the good Catholics, who loved processions and golden ornaments glittering in the sun, gathered at the customs point to receive, with due pomp, the episcopal blessing . . . a blessing mumbled in kitchen Latin and dispensed from the hand, not of Bishop Polyte, but of Polyte Lévesque, who crossed the American border in a Cadillac adorned with the crest of the bishopric, flanked by four Irish customs officers kneeling in the dust.

"Seems as though this particular bishop carried his own communion wine with him," Old Clovis adds, hard pressed to catch his breath.

Then, winking at Ti-Louis the Whistler:

"It's my opinion Monsignor Polyte has been teaching some of his tricks to our Dieudonné. I've a notion we'd better make it snappy and get on over to Lovers' Lane."

By dusk our two Don Quixotes had to elbow and shoulder their way to the oak at the end of Lovers' Lane. All Sainte-Marie-des-Côtes was there in a great state of effervescence and euphoria. The great question travelling from mouth to mouth was, would he come back or wouldn't he?

They consulted Old Clovis, who knew the ways of phantoms better than anybody. Wasn't it Clovis who, just the night before, had advised the wicked dead not to appear on All Saints' Day? And the ghost had obeyed.

"If that's the case," ventured one solitary onlooker standing under the tree, "it wasn't the ghost of Old Crache-à-Pic—because he's one sorcerer who never obeyed anybody."

Clovis took advantage of the attention being showered on him to instruct the ignorant on the real relationship between the living and the dead.

. . . The land of the dead is over there on the other side

of the horizon, you see, behind an invisible, transparent fence. On this side it's the land of the living with its stale pancakes, its spider webs, its Sunday mass, its squabbling neighbours, its high tides, its Marie-Pets, its misty moons foretelling bad weather—what we call life. On the other, protected by a big blue sheet attached to the four compass points, is the Great Beyond, also called the Land of the Dead. But sometimes the sheet rips or splits open, like wood that's too dry. This happens when there's a comet, for example, or just before a war or an earthquake. And on days like that the boldest and most curious of the dead stick their noses through the crack, and then, well, you've seen what happens.

The crowd is delighted. They slap the storyteller on the back.

"Go on, Clovis, tell us more!"

In listening so avidly to these stories about ghosts and the dead they've forgotten the most famous of them all, the very one who drew them here to the top of Lovers' Lane tonight. But the ghost in question hasn't forgotten. Here he is, faithful to the rendezvous.

"Mamma!"

A child cries out and at the same instant gets a slap from its mother. Two simultaneous reactions, you couldn't say which preceded which. Mother and son saw the same vision at the same time. She struck out from fear and sur-prise, the same reasons he yelped in the first place. Two reflex reactions. They'd been perfectly ready, prepared for anything, at any moment. But can you ever really say you're ready—in the dark of the night—for the sight of a phantom jigging its limbs on either side of its rib cage, a ghost so aggressive and lively?

A dried-up voice manages to croak, "Make room for him there!"

And then. . . .

Solemnly, majestically, stiffly, its joints freshly oiled and its bones chalked white, down it comes from its tree and glides across the King's Highway with the grace of a figure-skater. The crowd holds its breath in mute admiration. How light a soul is, cut loose from its body! It twists and spins, disappearing each time it turns away, like some discreet, prudish ghost disinclined to show its backside. Then it reappears facing frontwards, as nerve-racking and mysterious as ever. It's so wonderfully horrifying that the witnesses of this vision almost forget it's a vision and stretch out welcoming arms. They're on the point of calling out "Make yourself at home!" as the custom is around here. And you'd say the ghost itself was on the verge of answering, that it was ready to rejoin the living, who panic and withdraw, stepping on each others' feet, as they see it come closer.

Then, suddenly, the mystery becomes doubly mysterious; the apparition multiplies. What's going on? There's two of them now, two ghosts, one on the heels of the other! The new one is skinny as a beanpole, faintly white, knock-kneed. What a wreck! . . . And now, all of a sudden, it turns on the other ghost, takes off after it, tries to punch . . . no, it looks more like it's trying to hug it. Maybe this is Crache-à-Pic's son, the one who was lost at sea . . . yes, it must be. He's trying to catch up to his father who's resisting, struggling, wants to get away. . . . It's a free-for-all, a ghostly rumpus! The one trying to dance and put on some kind of a show, and the other trying to sneak away. Would father and son have some kind of score to settle between them? The kind of thing that never gets solved in a lifetime?

It's the son who wins, chasing the older ghost off the King's Highway and remaining sole master of the place. Swaggering, grimacing, agitated, swivelling on his spine, this

one has no hesitation in turning his back to the public . . .
back or backside! The crowd collected at the top of Lovers'
Lane applauds his victory. He dances and gesticulates like a
marionette, and is trying to bow when . . . whoops! something breaks in the region of his neck and his head drops
forward, rocks back and forth, suddenly straightens up, then
plops into his hands.

Then nothing. He disappears in turn. The battle of
the ghosts is over.

The people of Sainte-Marie-des-Côtes and the back
country, from Cocagne, Grand-Digue, Pré-d'en-Haut, and
Village-des-Trois-Maisons, stand dumbfounded, staring at each
other with haggard eyes. They are awaking from a common
dream — and the dream has burst like a bubble. They are all
that's left at the crossroads of Lovers' Lane and the King's
Highway: the fishermen, lumberjacks, and poachers, the
planters of cabbage and beets, the women and children, the
Hallowe'en trick-or-treaters and the watchers over the Dead,
the loudmouths, tongue-waggers, thrill-seekers, and rain-
machine salesmen.

Old Clovis is the first to break out laughing.

Then the laugh spreads from Pré-d'en-Haut to Grand-
Digue to Cocagne to the whole of Sainte-Marie-des-Côtes,
which rolls and rocks like the sea the day after a storm.

On the coast they were specialists in tracing the chain of
cause and effect, and in rendering unto Caesar what was
properly Caesar's, often to the detriment of the Good Lord
himself. They knew, for example, the exact date young
Crache-à-Pic had returned from her trip round the world,
and they realized that since that day they'd lived some of
their best moments since hard times had begun.

And according to Clovis those times go back to. . . .

So render unto the Crache-à-Pic girl what was properly hers: the president's wine in the barrels in the cowfield, the treasure-hunt through dunes and woods, the monkeyshines and face-making right under the noses of the bootleggers, and finally this open-air spectacle, this battle of ghosts offered gratis to the Depression poor who couldn't have afforded as much as a cock-fight. Once again it was Dieudonné who invented a scheme to hoodwink the law, and Crache-à-Pic who turned it into a joyful masquerade.

Black Willy could have killed her.

Not so fast, Black Willy, not just yet. Dieudonné was more farsighted than his men. He could see, for example, when he heard the details of this last adventure, that instead of working a marionette on the end of a string, you could manipulate the puppeteer. It was clear that Crache-à-Pic had shown a marked taste for theatre on this night of the Day of the Dead. Crache-à-Pic and her crowd of fellow loafers, who asked nothing better than to applaud any distraction that would make them forget their empty bellies. And although they'd seen through the mystery of the ghost at the second apparition, they had remained stunned by the artistic shock of this, the most extraordinary exhibition ever offered free to all comers in the midst of the Depression. A full-fledged spectacle, an outdoor magic show complete with prologue, mystery, clowning, complication, pantomime, reversal, and happy ending. And the whole thing set against a backdrop of leafless birch and aspen, at the foot of an enormous oak that seemed planted there specially to frame this farce for two performers. All that was missing from this devilry was the dialogue. . . .

"Black Willy, go back to Lovers' Lane and string up your ghost again."

"Hey! Just a minute. . . ."

"And this time make it talk."

Talk now, is it? But hasn't his boss caught on? Nobody believes in ghosts any more. They've seen through the trick. There has to be a better way to draw the crowd and the officers off the scent. . . .

"You mean. . . ."

Black Willy begins to understand. It's not the ghost that matters, it's the distraction. And for that, two ghosts are better than one. The important thing is to keep the show going as long as possible, long enough to unload the four schooners anchored on the horizon and move their cargoes along the back roads that join the coast to the main road north. North to the kingdom of Polyte Lévesque.

"In two nights we've already unloaded one. Get your skeleton act back on the road, Black Willy."

This time Black Willy was caught out again. Yet he had thought everything through: Crache-à-Pic would be back, of course, with one, perhaps two ghosts; they would be much more sophisticated — no matter! The bootlegger would let her have the better role, the last word, all the spectacular effects. As long as the show went on until the small hours of the morning, keeping everyone over in Lovers' Lane . . . while three miles farther north, at the top of Potter's Road, a line of trucks swung out onto the King's Highway. . . .

Black Willy had accounted for everything . . . except for what happened about midnight.

Up till then things were evolving according to plan. The ghosts had appeared one after the other, then together, teasing and provoking each other and having a good old-

fashioned wrangle, much to the amusement of the spectators. Then suddenly, without warning, the younger of the
two — the one the crowd had chosen to call Crache-à-Pic's
son — disappeared and bobbed up a few minutes later, a
little more to the north. Father Crache-à-Pic had no choice
but to follow. As did the rest of the crowd.

It was only at the third or fourth shift of scene that
Black Willy caught on: the ghosts were quietly leading the
assembly, policed by all those officers of the law, up to the
top of Potter's Road.

Old Clovis never actually did admit to my father, who
suspected as much, that he was the one behind this new
ploy of Crache-à-Pic's. All he would say was that from her
first year back on the coast she had been able to prove that
she had more wit than all the smugglers put together, and
that Dieudonné would have to polish up his act.

So Dieudonné's trucks, scared off by the delighted cries
of the crowd following the strolling players, barely had time
to turn around and try to find their way back to the coast,
running with no lights through the brambles and broken
branches.

That autumn the people of the coast had plenty of
time to discover all the sideroads that linked the sea to the
highway, for night after night the perambulating theatre
moved north, notch by notch, springing up unexpectedly,
apparently innocently, at just the right place and time to
make any truck bold enough to stick its nose out of the
bush turn tail in a hurry.

The worst of it was, the weather had taken the smugglers' side that year, providing the longest and finest Indian
summer the coast could remember. Twelve days of May
breezes and June sun in mid-November! The wild geese

changed direction and flew back north; the flies came out of the barns; squirrels ate up their winter store of nuts; cows wanted to calf, cod to spawn, and salmon to swim up-river. A little more of the same and the maples would have started to bud. It was an autumn to make Dieudonné and his gang dream of taking over the Madawaska market and overthrowing big boss Polyte Lévesque himself.

But the crowd gleefully following the travelling marionette show had invaded and conquered all the territory stretching between Sainte-Marie-des-Côtes and Village-des-Trois-Maisons. All they left the smugglers, to finish unloading the three schooners and their cargo of the finest Caribbean rum, were a few wheelbarrow tracks across the fields.

The first snowstorm, blown in on a mid-November north-east squall, swept Indian summer away in a single night, buried the frozen bones of the skeletons, and sent the crowd of spectators back to their winter tales by the fireside. The foreign schooners — which had supposedly come to sell laths and planks to a people who didn't even have the wherewithal to build themselves a doghouse, and had lain at anchor three miles off the coast for weeks — barely had time to hoist sail and make for the open sea, still as heavily laden as when they'd arrived.

Once again Crache-à-Pic had steered her band of Galoshes straight through the plans of Dieudonné and his gang. What a devil!

Before she married her guy from the north, Célestine was the widow of the only son of Cyprien Doucet, and had inherited from her father-in-law a house, some outbuildings, two woodsheds, and half a barn — the other half having disappeared in a cyclone come in from the sea, the only one to ravage the country since sorcerer Crache-à-Pic's hurricane, and this time a wind specializing not in steeples but haylofts. As luck would have it, Cyprien had parked his hay rake, harrows, and plough on the west side of the barn that fall, and had piled his hay on the side nearest the sea. So he lost his hay but saved his machinery. He died the same year, leaving his daughter-in-law one piece of advice for her widowhood:

"That witch of a wind feeds on salt hay. Keep the buildings."

The next day Célestine sold twelve acres of good hay meadow. Sold it to Dieudonné, who at that time was buying up fields the way Old Clovis bought bootlaces.

"Hmph!" chuckled the old man. "If I had as many pairs of boots as Dieudonné has acres of land, I wouldn't need to bother getting my shoes resoled."

According to Clovis, if the snow hadn't stopped him Dieudonné could have ploughed and planted his lands year in year out without ever passing the plough in the same furrow. His fences came up out of the sea, skirted the cemetery, wound past the convent lands, and zigzagged around the pioneer farms of the parish, encircling them, closing them in, strangling them until they cried for mercy. And the poor little ancestral lands, barely good enough to grow a little wild mustard and thistles, finally yielded and fell under Dieudonné's ploughs.

Along with the fields, the barns and buildings came under Dieudonné's dominion too. Especially them, for they were what the bootlegger most coveted. And had for the past five years. Cabins in good repair, machine sheds, a barn cut cleanly in two, a huddle of outbuildings, all were ideal shelters where he could dig hiding places to bury his bottles. He tried to twist Célestine's arm.

"Name your price," he told her a few weeks before

All Saints' Day. But Célestine was thinking of her children. And even more of her guy from the north, who in less than five years had managed to drink up the price of twelve acres of good land and give her three extra kids into the bargain. Célestine figured she shouldn't let her cabins and her half-barn go the same way, so once more she told Dieudonné no.

To refuse this short-tempered ogre anything in those years was about as risky as running a horse race on the ice in the bay at the time of the spring thaw. But Clovis would tell you that, forced to eke out a living between the squall and the tempest, folks on the coast have learned to bend without bowing, and that . . .

". . . every year, at the time of the spring thaw, you can see them running trotting races on the bay."

This being the case, Célestine could risk saying no to Dieudonné. And the whole village applauded her. Every needy farmer who had let his family land go for a mouthful of bread applauded Célestine's courage and tenacity.

Everyone except her husband.

"Big loony," he said. "Dieudonné's even letting you set your own price. For three cabins and half a barn you could squeeze enough out of him to feed your children for years."

Célestine gave her man a sidelong look and said nothing.

"The bootlegger must really want those buildings something desperate. In your place. . . ."

In Célestine's place the whole country would have given in long ago, including those needy farmers encouraging her to hold out now. Yes, they'd have made everyone sup on dishonour. But when one single person stands up to Dieudonné, why, the whole coast carries its head high.

"And what's he need another roof for, with all the buildings he's already got in the palm of his hand?"

A superfluous question. Everyone knew the answer. The day Dieudonné became master of all the relay points between the sea and the King's Highway, no policeman in the land would be able to foil him. He'd have fine sport rolling his jugs and barrels from one shed to another right between the officers' legs, without giving a single official nose time for a whiff.

Some even dared suggest that a secret passage joined the sea-caves of the cape to one of Dieudonné's buildings. Médard claimed that the tunnel passed right under his land, and Melchior said it came up in the Babineaus' barn.

So why Célestine's buildings? Why did Dieudonné want them so badly? Might it be that her father-in-law, Cyprien, was such an inveterate old treasure-seeker that he'd dug holes in all his fields, so they said, and Dieudonné would only have to join them up with underground passages?

They gabbed and glossed and thumbed over possibilities like beads on a rosary. And all the while Célestine continued to hold out. How long would the duel go on? In the end Dieudonné would get mad and twist this Madeleine de Verchères' neck.

"When he's finished twisting her arm enough first, I'm afraid he'll. . . ."

But the boss of the bootleggers discovered a solution that was more honourable and less risky: intimidation. One day he sent that impudent little runt Philias over to deliver to Célestine's husband, by hand, a tattered, yellowing piece of paper, an old contract he had dug up from a trunk in the attic that held a lot of ten-year-old account books.

"What's that?" the guy from the north asked nervously.

"It's for your Célestine," swaggered the messenger. "Dieudonné sends to say she hasn't settled this account here. He wants payment within a week. With interest."

Célestine's man turned pale. Sell, yes — he was ready to sell his shirt..But pay? Pay old bills hanging around since the time of the late Cyprien? And he grabbed little Philias by the throat.

"You son of a bitch!" he yelled in the poor errand-boy's teeth, while the latter struggled and shouted to his assailant to let go, that he had nothing to do with it, and that Dieudonné would get even.

The name Dieudonné calmed the guy from the north's fury, for he hadn't yet given up the idea of selling his wife's property.

"What's your boss want? What's he asking?"

"Read."

The guy from the north read.

"Holy Bejeezus!"

Then he softened his tone and changed tack; there must be some way to negotiate. This document put a nice, clean knife to their throats. And wasn't it just like that crafty old codger Cyprien to leave them a gift like that on his death-bed — a bill overdue for ten years!

"How come Dieudonné only came across that damned paper today?"

Philias sensed his adversary's confusion and swelled up a little.

"He does a big spring-cleaning once a year."

"And this year it just happens his spring falls in the month of November?"

Little Philias chose to laugh to relax his nerves.

"He . . . ha-ha . . . found it just like that . . . in a trunk in the attic, he says."

"At the bottom of a trunk in the attic, you say?"

And little Philias had the impression that Dieudonné had just won an ally.

"That's it," he said.

"So that's it, is it?" Célestine exclaimed when she heard about the paper that was going to take the bread out of her children's mouths. And that same evening the ten-year-old contract spelling out Cyprien Doucet's debt to Dieudonné passed from Célestine's hands to her cousin Céleste's, and from there to the hands of her goddaughter and protégée, Crache-à-Pic.

"So that's it, is it?" snaps Crache-à-Pic in turn. "We'll see about that!"

She examines the paper closely, fingering and sniffing it with care.

"A bunch of shit, that's what it is," she concludes. "Rip that up, Célestine, and throw it in the fire. It's a fake."

A fake?

The two cousins are speechless.

"The paper's yellowed over a lantern flame, I tell you, and the edges were shredded with a razor blade."

Céleste and Célestine blink their eyes.

"Are you sure?"

Crache-à-Pic tightens her lips and frowns.

"But he's no fool, the bugger. If he sent you that paper there, Célestine, you can be sure he made two copies; he'll be keeping the other nice and warm in his hip pocket."

At last Célestine lets her arms fall to her sides. She's sworn to stand up to big Dieudonné for the future of her children, in memory of her father-in-law and her first husband, and for the honour of it, too, out of a sense of dignity.

But now she's at the end of her tether. She's a woman surrounded by orphans — might as well call them that, for even
though her second husband is still alive, he has reduced his
offspring to that state. She's in no position to drag the richest and most powerful man on the coast before the courts.

Crache-à-Pic smiles . . . that magnificent smile of her
moments of inspiration.

"And do you think Dieudonné has any hankering to
appear before the judges, even to get hold of your barn?"

"But he wouldn't need to go to court to take my
property. With a paper like that he could just send around
any old bailiff, I couldn't say a thing."

Crache-à-Pic clenches her fists.

"We'll see whether or not you have anything to say.
Leave me the paper."

Céleste, who hasn't said a word yet, looks out at the
apple tree where they buried the first Crache-à-Pic so long
ago.

"An eye for an eye and a tooth for a tooth," she says.

And so it was that two days later Dieudonné received
in person, from the hands of Jimmy-the-Flea, a paper every
bit as yellowed and tattered as the document he had sent
Célestine. This second contract, copied word for word from
the first, charged Monsieur Dieudonné to settle with the
heirs of the late Crache-à-Pic a debt that was thirty years old
and came out, with interest, to the exact sum of Old Cyprien's
debt.

Dieudonné reread the document three times over. Then
he fingered it, smelled it, and let out a whistle of admiration.
Crache-à-Pic had passed him on the outside. A double
counterfeit. She had copied his idea, his ink, his procedures,
his tricks — she had copied the copier, the bitch! What nerve!
For the first time the bootlegger saw that the young she-

wolf had never invented a thing, had never taken the lead; from the minute she'd stepped on stage, she had simply put her feet into his own footsteps. Under his breath he said,

"Nobody ever sent my own spit back in my face before." And automatically he wiped his face with the back of his hand.

Funny little fish, this Jimmy-the-Flea. It's the first time Dieudonné has had him on the end of his line . . . he looks him over from head to tail, and follows up his line of thought. For months now someone has been ferreting around in his most secret business. The president's password, his hideouts, the ghost. . . . This Jimmy-the-Flea is Céleste's son and Céleste, as her name shows, is cousin on the female side to Célestine, that stubborn daughter-in-law of the late Cyprien. But there the scent fades. Yet someone has been rifling his barn and his house. Witness this document: same paper, same ink, same way of making the letters. . . . In a country like this, everybody is someone's son- or brother-in-law and everyone else's cousin, so how do you steer clear of relations?

Suddenly Dieudonné stiffens.

"Great God!" he says between his teeth, "why didn't I think of it!"

And turning his bulk towards the kitchen:

"Zéphirine!"

Slowly Zéphirine draws her head out of the oven, wipes her hands on her apron, and in her felt mules slipslops into her lord and master's presence.

Jimmy-the-Flea is standing on one leg and then the other, looking for a window, a door ajar, some possible exit.

"Zéphirine," says Dieudonné, "you know Célestine-à-Charlitte Grelot. Delve me her family connection with the Damiens of l'Anse-aux-Outardes."

Zéphirine, whose breath has sunk down into her felt

slippers, takes a certain time to reply. But in the end she recites, like a lesson she's learned too quickly and is afraid of forgetting before the last word is out:

"The Damiens-à-Jude of L'Anse-aux-Outardes are related in the third degree by the branch of the maternal grandfather to old Charles called Charlitte LeBlanc who came and settled at the end of Jacquot's Point at the beginning of the last century. I have that from my mother who had it from hers who was one of the pioneers as you might say of the same point that was named after the name of her man."

Dieudonné blinks, snuffles two or three incomprehensible words, and dismisses his servant who, in passing, lashes out a look at Jimmy-the-Flea that says, "Don't let me catch you laughing, you little good-for-nothing!"

That same night the two cousins and the Galoshes celebrated their victory with a joyful task, hauling the *Sea-Cow* up on land before the ice closed in.

When Célestine got home, her man was sitting on the woodbox waiting for her. He had emptied a mickey of rum and was whistling between his teeth. Her older boys had locked the little ones in the bedroom and were standing with their backs to the door, not saying a word. Célestine saw the drunkard take up the poker and start for her. She could see it all coming. He had never beaten her before, and she wondered how she would react. She managed to duck the first blow but the second caught her on the hip. At their mother's cry the boys left their guard post and tackled their stepfather with flying fists. At the same instant Ti-Louis the Whistler pushed open the door.

Célestine's nephew was small and slight but quick as a squirrel. Shooting a leg out, he tripped up the drunkard.

Then, standing over him, he wrenched away the poker; and after seeing his aunt and the little ones into the attic, he sent his uncle sprawling onto the bed with a kick in the rear.

"Let him snore it off until morning, the son of a bitch."

And he threw the poker into the bottom of the woodbox.

The explanations between husband and wife didn't take place until next day. Célestine had loved this man with his sad-dog eyes, and had thought she'd found in him a father for her children. In those days any widow with orphans aspired to a normal home with a head of the family to cut wood, fix the roof, go off to the woods or the sea, and teach the sons to become men. So Célestine had welcomed her guy from the north as a saviour.

"It's the bootleggers' fault," Old Clovis used to say later to Ti-Louis. "It was those brutes who got him drinking. Drink's not made for a man with sad eyes. It's made for men who have solid hearts and joyful souls. Like you and me."

Her man wasn't really bad, and Célestine was ready to forgive him. She was willing to forget the whole incident and not even require promises of future temperance . . . you don't take a dog's bone away from him. But she wouldn't sell her property to Dieudonné. That issue was closed.

It might be closed for Célestine, her husband, and the kids, but what about the nephew? Ti-Louis was too sensitive not to feel the aversion he inspired in his uncle. And the aversion was mutual and worrisome, for it drove the youth to believe that he was the secret cause of the discord between man and wife. So the first time the drunkard said a few words to the effect that times were too hard to let a poor family feed an extra mouth, the orphan from the States shoved his harmonica in his coat pocket, and took down his burlap sack from the nail on the wall and laid it ready at the foot of his bed.

Next morning Célestine found a page from the calendar left on the kitchen table, and scribbled across the last days of November:

Don't worry bout me.
I'll make out.
                          Ti-Louis

"Tobie? . . ."

Crache-à-Pic searched the barn, the shed where the fishing tackle was kept, the beached schooner. Then she came back to the house and climbed the ladder to the loft. Finally she took the dirt road that linked their place to Céleste's, and together the two women went over to the Twins'.

About noon Old Clovis joined the Galoshes, alerting his three poacher cronies who came along armed with eel-spears, hatchets, and harpoons . . . you never know . . . and by five o'clock Long-Tongue Médard had told Jeannette, who had told Marie-Pet, who had knocked long and hard on the presbytery door. Whereupon the *curé* immediately sent his servant to advise Constable Martial, while he himself donned his biretta and took the road to Cap-Lumière.

. . . He heard them calling his name: To-bie! To-bie! . . . That struck him. Then amused him. His name . . . the only thing that was really his, his very own. . . . He's never hurt anybody, it's not his fault. Nothing that happens is his fault.

Sometimes he burns himself with the soup, it's always too hot, it's not his fault. One day he was afraid of a dog, Xavier-the-Hunchback's dog who had a hump on his back too, like Xavier. He thought the dog wanted to bite but his mother had reassured him.

"He just wants to play," she said.

And she'd thrown a ball to the dog, who picked it up and played with it happily. Since then he's never been afraid of dogs. Nor of the animals in the stable who eat out of his hand. Or the ones in the Twins' barn that he used to go over and caress early in the morning in the days when the Twins were still farming. But Adal-Gobert sold their cattle one after another, and let the mare die because they said she was too old to plough. And then it was the sea, and the Twins had to go out every morning after cod and mackerel, which meant that Tobie got used to rubbing his palm on the timbers of the empty stable and talking the language of the animals to the rafters. . . . One day he tried to get close to the chickens, but they took fright without understanding what he wanted. They all rushed off with a terrible cackling as if Tobie wanted to kill them. That made him sad, and since then he hasn't gone back to the henhouse. Sometimes he goes down to the beach early in the morning to talk to the seabirds. The ones he likes best are the herons, but they won't let him get close because they're afraid he'll break their legs, as thin as knitting needles. There's always the forest. But that's forbidden. His mother, Céleste, Crache-à-Pic too, have all warned him about the forest.

"It's dark in the woods," says Céleste. "You don't want to risk it."

So Tobie hasn't. He's always been afraid of the dark. Every evening he closes his eyes before blowing out the lamp so he won't have to see the emptiness of the night. No, he's never gone near the forest. But this morning he saw the sun light up the apple trees in the back yard, and all the other trees too because they'd turned white from top to root. Snow had fallen in big torn flakes during the night and white-washed the whole countryside. Tobie looked everywhere, from back yard, to frozen sea, to forest. And the whitest part of all this life surrounding the house was the woods. He didn't tell Crache-à-Pic. There was no sense, she was sleeping. The forest was white as a sheet, no danger there — to begin with it amused him to see the trail of his foot-steps stretching behind him, but in the end he lost track of them, for it began to snow again. . . . The woods aren't at all like the dark forest he imagined. He enters them gently, almost on tiptoe, like walking down the aisle of a church lit by chandeliers hanging like icicles. The branches of the birch trees meet overhead almost like hands in prayer. Perfectly white. Now and then a squirrel scampers along a bent tree trunk sweeping the snow down with his tail. Tobie gets a clump in the face. Then two jack-rabbits stop in full flight to warn him . . . to warn him of what? He feels so good in this tunnel halfway between hot and cold, between heaven and earth, between life and dream. For the first time in his life Tobie feels really at home, alone with the animals at the heart of their world. The jack-rabbits run by again, this time without stopping. And behind them comes a bundle of brown fur unwinding like a gigantic ball of wool. Tobie watches, wide-eyed, not moving. The ball of wool stretches and out comes a neck, four paws. Tobie's first reflex is to remember Xavier-the-Hunchback's dog who frightened him. But his mother told him the dog only wanted to play. All animals want to play. Or else they run away like the herons and the chickens. . . . Now the snow is falling in heavy flakes. The paws of the ball of wool are sinking into it. This animal isn't used to winter, thinks Tobie, and he feels sorry for him, wants to help him. Once again a reflex restrains his arm. Now they're face to face, the bear and the boy, studying each other.

"To-bie! . . . To-bie!"

It's Crache-à-Pic's voice. Crache-à-Pic and Céleste. The bear lifts his head at the same time as Tobie. They listen together. Then Tobie reaches out to the bear to protect him . . . don't be afraid . . . it's my sister . . . she just wants to play. . . . The bear opens its jaws and whines. . . . No, no, old fellow, don't be afraid. . . . Tobie puts his arms around the furry neck . . . encircles it without squeezing, or barely, and snuggles up to the bear's side. No one's calling now. They've lost the trail. Tobie will be left alone.

Reddish light filters between the trees, flashes like lightning, disappears, then comes back again. It's the sun setting. The sun's sticking his head through the bars of his bed before he goes to sleep, thinks Tobie. Then he doesn't think of anything any more.

It's been a long night for Crache-à-Pic. The longest she has known since her father disappeared at sea. But it was her mother who sat out that endless night. This time she is the one to bear the load, alone, sole captain of the household, the only one responsible. She came back in the spring to be at her mother's deathbed and to take charge of her heritage, whose one solitary asset was named Tobie.

All night long the priest, the constable, the neighbours, and Old Clovis and his pals succeeded each other in the Crache-à-Pic house on Cap Lumière. The men came and

went from the sea to the edge of the woods calling, "Tobie!
. . . Tobie! . . ." But only Crache-à-Pic and Céleste never closed
an eye.

And the Twins.

A little after midnight Crache-à-Pic asked Céleste what
had become of Adalbert-Dagobert. Had they taken to the
woods? In the snow?

. . . .

Not the woods, no, Crache-à-Pic. The Twins followed
the road to the bootlegger's place. Right up to big
Dieudonné's door, and roused him out of bed. And there
a strange scene took place, almost without words. The
Twins looked the smuggler straight in the eye till he blinked.
Then the smuggler grew defensive, pretended not to understand. But Dagobert wouldn't let go, and Adalbert backed
him up, and their double silence was so heavy that poor
Dieudonné struggled in it like a devil in a holy-water font.

. . . But how do you expect anyone to do anything in
this thick snow, in the middle of the night?

. . . By morning the snow will have stopped and the
sun will light up the forest.

. . . But why him? If all the men from three villages
around haven't been able to do anything. . . .

. . . Because Dieudonné has the means to do it.

. . . The means? What means? What's money got to do
with a young fellow lost in the woods?

. . . Hidden in one of his barns in the fields above
Champdoré, Dieudonné has a. . . .

Hold your tongue!

No, the Twins won't. It's a question of Tobie's life.

. . . But Tobie's a poor half-wit who'll never be able to
take care of himself.

. . . All the more reason.

Dieudonné twists and turns and tries to send the Twins back to Cap-Lumière. Go back and sleep on it. Tomorrow he'll let them know.

. . . Maybe tomorrow will be too late.

. . . But do they at least realize the cost of what they're asking, and all for nothing, more than likely? Do these Twins who seemed so well informed about bootleggers' hiding places have any notion of how important it is for Dieudonné to keep his comings and goings secret? And to keep secret, too, . . .

"Nobody knows anything about my barn in Champ-doré, nor what's inside it. And you expect me to throw it wide open to the eyes of the bailiffs and the constable?"

The Twins don't answer. They just stand there, staring at the bootlegger.

When Constable Martial made out the shape of a bear following Tobie, putting its paws in his tracks, he took Old Crache-à-Pic's rifle down from the wall and checked the breech. But instinctively Céleste grabbed it from him. And Crache-à-Pic made everyone go up to the attic.

"And don't let me hear a whisper," she said.

Then she went out the back door all alone and walked gently, barely crushing the snow sparkling in the morning sun, to meet her brother and the bear. The introductions took place right there in the middle of the field, not far from the apple tree where her grandfather had been secretly buried thirty years before.

When the rescuers and watchers could at last come down from the attic and go out in the yard, the first sight that met their eyes was a little airplane zigzagging and circling above their heads. Clovis swore to my father years afterwards that it had been flying low enough to spot Tobie and the bear, who were calmly coming home, because with his own eyes Clovis had been able to recognize Dieudonné in the cockpit, flanked by the twins Adalbert-Dagobert.

So it had been a useless gesture on Dieudonné's part, and one that unmasked him as secret pilot of a smugglers' airplane. But it was none the less a gesture that made the whole of this habitually mocking, scandal-mongering country bow its head and raise its eyes to heaven.

"In the future," concluded Old Clovis back in his forge, "they'd just have to count on an extra mouth to feed. It certainly looks as if that old ghost Crache-à-Pic had decided to come back personally to protect his descendants from the dangers of life."

"But it's a real bear, Clovis!"

"I know it's a bear. So what? . . . "

CHAPTER THREE

DURING THE MONTH OF ADVENT TI-LOUIS THE WHISTLER asked himself every day, since winter was so solidly established, could spring be far behind? Breathe deeply, Ti-Louis, take a deep breath, you'll get to snap at March's heels yet.... And he did breathe deeply, drawing the air right down to the bottom of his lungs, imagining that along with each gulp of air he was swallowing a bit of bird-food.

Four weeks without a bed or a pillow for his head, without a clean shirt or a place at table, without even once untying his boots. He had rediscovered his old habit of hunting out scraps set aside for the chickens or the pigs. He relearned how to sneak into a stable at night. But he slept with only one eye shut. He must on no account be caught and brought back to his aunt's, causing Célestine trouble. After all, he was young and resourceful; he'd find a way to get through the winter all right. A winter's only five months — sometimes six — at the very worst, in a bad year, seven.

One night he stumbled on one of the smugglers' cars laid up for the winter. A Buick, chrome-trimmed, spacious, solid, its four doors locked but not quite foolproof. There was no one around so he slept in it for an hour or two. But about midnight the cold woke him and he realized he'd have to get up and walk. Too bad, the Buick was as comfortable as a real bed. He walked a good part of the night to keep from freezing. Then towards morning he found another car in an unlocked garage and buried himself in it like a bear in its hole.

. . . A bear. To think that Tobie had brought a wild bear back from the forest. And that it was now quietly hibernating in the Crache-à-Pics' back yard. If only Ti-Louis had been able to turn into a bear for the winter. A bear must never have his muzzle or paws or the skin of his heart frozen . . . and Ti-Louis fell asleep at dawn dreaming that bit by bit his skin was growing a thick coat of silky fur. The sun was already high when he woke with frozen ears, not having given his dream long enough to change them into a bear's. So the next night he determined to push his luck and sleep in forbidden territory.

He waited till the lights in the houses of Cap-Lumière were out and the dogs had stopped barking. Then he made the sign of the cross . . . in the name of the Father and so on . . . spat in his hands and took the plunge. The bear was sleeping in a lair that Tobie and Céleste had dug for him at the foot of the apple tree and had filled with twigs and dry leaves. Ti-Louis knew from his father that a bear will sleep for several months if he's not disturbed . . . if he's not disturbed. Would a bear consider it a disturbance to feel a timid breath and the contact of a slim body, the body of a lad who feeds on air? The very thought of his hunger set Ti-Louis trembling.

"What if," he said to himself, shivering in his bones, "what if, all of a sudden, the bear feels hungry too? Would I hesitate to eat a rabbit, a nice fat warm rabbit, if I caught one tomorrow morning sleeping alongside me?"

So the orphan from the States left the Crache-à-Pics' yard and set off again in search of an empty automobile.

By the last Sunday in Advent Ti-Louis's backside knew every spring in every seat of every car the bootleggers had camouflaged for the winter in barns, sheds, and lean-tos. He could present to you, as though they were members of his own family, the Cadillac with its steering wheel sheathed in green velvet, which in its splendour he had baptized *Mae West*; the convertible whose four wheels squeaked in harmony, so he nicknamed it *The Accordion*; the Babineaus' big slow Lincoln which always seemed to be on a holiday, so he called it *The Loafer*; and the Buick reserved for Black Willy's nocturnal escapades, doubly well named *Moonshine*. Plus assorted pick-ups, trucks, vans, and the hearse.

A hearse! What a find for the homeless! Roomy enough to let a young man stretch out full length, legs stiff, hands crossed on his chest, his mind in the clouds and his feet frigid. But next morning he woke quite surprised to find himself still in the land of the living, and spent all day questioning his ultimate purpose in life. The following night he went back to sleeping in the ample bosom of *Mae West*.

It was in the plush comfort of the beautiful Cadillac that Ti-Louis the Automobile Bum woke with a start one December night, to hear two of Dieudonné's men chiding each other: "Not so loud! . . . You'd wake the dead. . . . Shh! . . . Quit shoving!" And Ti-Louis barely had time to jump out of his *Mae West* and hide behind the woodpile.

At first he didn't realize the extent of the catastrophe. To tell the truth, nobody knew what was going on right away. The sequence of events that had begun the night before had now taken on such a rhythm that even Old Clovis had to dust the cobwebs out of his brain to get them in the right order.

... It all began with the appearance of a strange customer at the reception desk of Sainte-Marie-des-Côte's only hotel: a red and white Father Christmas with beard and curls and a big laugh and such an accent. . . . Well, well, now! And Tim Robichaud rushed off to warn the bottleggers. Ever since the good Christian folk of the coast had banished Santa Claus from the liturgical calendar to leave more room for Baby Jesus, it was a rare thing to see a Father Christmas — especially one come all the way over from the capital to stick oranges in the socks of the kids from the coast. So, from Tim to Pierre to Paul, word soon reached Black Willy's ear.

In a similar way, the summer before, the barns and sheds of the coast had received the following news-flash from the hotel at Cocagne:

"A coffee-grinder salesman is doing the rounds of the country."

The bootleggers had had no trouble whatsoever seeing that such a salesman was right off base in a country where everyone drank regular, cherry-stem, or tansy tea. So they hurried off to camouflage their cars under their haystacks. The Royal Canadian Mounted Police had tried to pick the most neutral and inconspicuous-looking hotel on the coast. Clovis could have told them to take the first one handy, because all the hotels around here look that way. But Clovis didn't go sticking his nose in other people's business back in 1930.

The big problem for the Mounties was that they never came down this way except in times of great danger or grand ceremony . . . to escort the King of England, say, or to capture a murderer. But neither kings nor murderers spend much time around Sainte-Marie-des-Côtes — or Cocagne or Pré-d'en-Haut, for that matter — so it was hard for these Mounted Police to get to know the country.

" . . . the *mentality* of the country," Old Clovis corrected, waving his forefinger.

Since due to their calling the bootleggers were bound to supply their customers in great secrecy, they had got used to supplying their own needs in a shroud of secrecy as well. None the less they had a good idea of the source of those Cadillacs, Buicks, and Lincolns they procured at night in exchange for loads of rum or whisky. That's why they thought it prudent not to let any coffee-grinder salesman search their barns or garages — at least, not until they'd remodelled their haystacks, which at the end of August 1930 took on some remarkable dimensions and shapes. The locals would stand out on their front porches in admiration of these huge, outlandish, hunchbacked haycocks with their heavily rounded shoulders and hips and swelled-up middles, like gigantic, overstuffed ladybugs. How playful these coast farmers could get at haytime! And next day, from the hands of Black Willy, the farmers would receive enough whisky to let them finish their haymaking without a moment's remorse.

"I might add that haymaking that year lasted right up to the time for hauling winter firewood."

And Old Clovis was taken with an interminable hiccough.

With Father Christmas, though, the smugglers were looking at a horse of a different colour. The haying season was well over. Even an inspector from the Mounted Police wouldn't be taken in for long by a dozen piles of snow lined up in a row, all exactly alike. Not to mention the fact that the midday sun was likely to raise a few blisters on those igloos, at which time Father Christmas would discover. . . .

"Philias!" yelled Black Willy as soon as he understood the message from the Hôtel Beau-Séjour.

And the rest of the day was taken up in endless palaver between Sainte-Marie-des-Côtes, Champdoré, Bois-Joli, and Village-des-Trois-Maisons. Unfortunately, Dieudonné had left the day before on a secret mission somewhere in Nova Scotia.

"The telegraph!" suggested one of the Damien boys. "Let's get orders from Dieudonné by telegraph."

. . . The telegraph . . . yes, the telegraph . . . a great thing, that telegraph, but . . . but Black Willy hated to admit to his bootlegging pals that after his double failure with the cows and the ghosts he was in disgrace, and that the telegraph code had been withheld to punish him.

The code? Was that all? Bah! Damien-à-Damien wasn't going to let his future ride on such a trifle. He knew the code by heart.

"Just let me at that telegraph," he said.

So Damien's loudmouth son set off for the haybarn, followed by all the others.

When a black box appeared from under the laths and hay, closed tighter than an oyster and wrapped up in its own wires, Damien's fingers grew a mite hesitant. That instant was all Black Willy needed to reaffirm his authority as foreman. He knew everything about handling these machines; it was spelling that gave him pause: Royal Canadian Mounted Police . . . Santa Claus. . . .

"Let me spell it for you," threw in Télesphore, who had quit school just a couple of years before.

So it was that two hours later, somewhere in the depths

of Nova Scotia, Dieudonné found himself trying to decipher a message written in Black Willy's words, with Télesphore's spelling, the Damien boy's encoding, and just about everybody's ideas.

"Goddamit!" he exclaimed. "What's going on back there?"

Later that day, Dieudonné's men swallowed back large lumps in their throats on receiving their boss's reply: "Dump all into the sea," the telegram read, encoded in English.

. . . !

It was the following night that Ti-Louis the Whistler was yanked from sleep in the arms of his *Mae West*.

What did they want with his sweetheart? Where were they taking her? Ti-Louis crept out from behind the woodpile and followed Joe Colossus and Little Philias, who were pushing the Cadillac through the field. . . . Look out, she'll never make it! The ditch is three feet deep at least, watch what you're doing! . . . She does make it, though; she reaches the road and rolls on towards her destiny. Ti-Louis can't believe his eyes. He runs after her, then turns abruptly and stares at the Babineaus' barn. . . . It's not possible! That's *The Loafer*, all decked out in white with frosted windows, thump-thumping along pushed by three guys in fur hats. They couldn't all be going to the same place, could they? And why in silence, in the middle of the night, with their lights out? What's going on? . . . Ti-Louis would like to shout, make them stop, try to understand, but he's pushed out of the way by a hired hand from Bois-Joli running ahead of *Moonshine*, driven by Black Willy, to show him the way. Her wheels get stuck in the frozen ruts and she stalls there in the middle of the road, poor thing, under a hail of oaths and kicks. Oh no! Not this! Ti-Louis grabs his stomach. . . . Not the hearse! But there it is on the headland, silhouetted against the sky like some nocturnal dragon squealing in every joint. A hearse? Travelling at night? What sort of a corpse . . . ? Don't ask too many questions, Ti-Louis, run after them, catch up with the procession. . . . Listen to that strange music coming over the snow . . . *The Accordion*, rattling, farting, spitting out acid notes on the frozen December air — there goes the little convertible, the youngest member of the family, off to join the others on the bay.

"The bay! Holy Mary Mother of God!"

In a flash Ti-Louis sees it all. His companions, his nighttime accomplices whom he knows like the back of his hand, his homes who have protected him against zero weather, his confidants, his friends . . . all being led off to the slaughter! He hears himself shouting,

"Stop! Stop that!"

But nothing will stop them. Off they go one after the other, boldly rolling out onto the ice of the bay, wheels in the ruts, radiator ornaments held high, hoods bravely pointed straight for the horizon. And the horizon is the open sea.

Later, choking back a sob, Ti-Louis the Whistler told Old Clovis the ending.

Each of the cars courageously approached the water's edge in total silence, lit only by the light of the moon. At the last moment the door flew open to eject a dazed bootlegger driver onto the ice. Then, gently nose-diving, raising their tailfins in the air, down they all plunged and disappeared into the depths of the sea.

Next day Dieudonné returned to discover that he'd lost the apple of his eye, that it had been a great mistake to leave his business to those dodos of henchmen for even three days

. . . can't you even decipher a code, you bunch of block-heads? . . . and that the RCMP had gone home empty-handed. And Clovis and the rest of the coast had a great laugh.

For the only person to do any sleeping at all the night of the mass automobile suicide had been the Santa Claus from Ottawa. Every house, except Hôtel Beau-Séjour, had had its windows thrown wide open in the moonlight to admire the strange procession going out on the bay. And the village counted the Lincoln, the Buick, the Oldsmobile, and the Cadillac, and was puffed with pride at such hidden riches. What did it matter that the little airplane had been discovered just after All Saints' Day, or that all those cars drowned just before Christmas? The whole country swelled with a sense of self-importance. As Melchior put it,

"It's not only that we're rich, we can even afford to chuck it away! I don't know another city in the country, be it Montréal or Toronto, where they get to celebrate Christmas by heaving rocks like that into the sea!"

And Gaspard added,

"And right under the nose of Santa Claus, snuggled up tight and snoring away in his feather bed!"

After Dieudonné and Black Willy, the chief mourner for *The Loafer*, *Moonshine*, and especially *Mae West* was Ti-Louis the Whistler. Starving and chilled to the bone, he roamed the fields in search of a barn, a stable, or a pigsty buried under the snow. Christmas Eve, he remembered, was the time that animals talk. . . . An old story of his father's, a legend or fable, had it that once a year, on Christmas Eve, the animals are given the gift of speech.

Ti-Louis resolutely pushes open the door of the Babineaus' barn and goes inside. Dark as the tomb. Dangerous, too. Might step on a hayfork or stumble over the blade of the mower. Little by little his eyes adapt to the dark; he makes out the plough, the seed-drill, the walls. He steps over a pile of lumber, a heap of straw, then hears something moving behind him. He stands stock still. Whatever you do, don't back up. Suddenly a strong smell of horse piss assails him, accompanied by the sound of a fountain splashing almost at his feet. He gives a low chuckle and turns around. In the dark he has crossed over into the stable and is standing right in the middle of the stall. He stretches out an arm and feels a muzzle, a mane, and the neck of a mare.

"Hi there, Blanche! Don't move on my account. Nobody move, I was only passing through. Just stay right there and go on with your conversation."

Now he can make out a cow and two heifers and in one corner a woolly sheep. Mmmm! What good cutlets must be hiding under its coat! The thought makes his mouth water. If he searches the barn . . . barns always have sickles and axes and good sharp knives. . . . The cow turns towards him and looks him straight in the eye. Ti-Louis is ashamed of himself. He nervously fiddles with her tail, twisting it into a crown around her rump.

"What was that you said?" he asks her, down on one knee.

But she has turned back to her cud, reassured.

"Could I just borrow a quart of milk, maybe?"

. . . .

"I promise you, your calves are fatter than I am . . . no offence meant. And besides, it's Christmas."

And joking with the animals, who now begin to bleat and moo and whinny to see who can speak the loudest, the guest of the stable starts hunting for a pail.

. . . Feeling around among shovels, rakes, curry-combs, harness, and wagon wheels, all of a sudden his fingers catch in a ring hidden under the straw on the floor. He pulls, and a trap door opens.

"What the devil . . . ? Do you know what . . . ?" he starts to ask the animals.

Down the trap door it's even darker than in the stable. He can see absolutely nothing. . . . Is it a cellar or a hideout? The word "hideout" sharpens his suspicions. The Babineaus' barn . . . the place that attracts so many red-nosed men, Aunt Célestine's husband among them, who always used to come out three sheets in the wind . . . . A hideout under the straw in the Babineaus' barn! And without wasting a second he reaches out an arm, explores with his fingers, and hauls up a one-gallon can. He takes it over to a beam of moonlight: a gallon can made of tin and stamped with the sign of a hand, the trademark of the foremost gang of smugglers on the coast.

"Hand Brand!" exclaims the starving Ti-Louis. "Dear little Christmas Jesus, thank you so much!"

And picking up the first pointed object he finds in the hay, he punctures the can and watches in amazement as a stream of golden whisky squirts into his face.

An hour later the animals in the stable are waggling their rear-ends to accompany the spasmodic song of their guest, who lies back in the straw singing,

Away in the . . . hic . . . manger,
No . . . hic . . . crib for a . . . hic . . . bed. . . .

All that night Clovis had tended his fire in the forge, while repeating his solemn warning to the flies:

"He'll come, seeing as it's Christmas he'll drop by. Which means, when he does, make sure you give him a good welcome."

As soon as he'd heard from Célestine the news of the

young orphan's hasty departure, Clovis had set out to look for him. He had first asked the people in Sainte-Marie-des-Côtes; they'd seen him headed for Grand-Digue, where he'd been seen doubling back to Champdoré, where somebody had seen him on the portage that leads to Village-des-Trois-Maisons. Someone in Bois-Joli claimed to have recognized him one night sleeping in the box of a truck that belonged to one of Dieudonné's hired hands.

"But when I went to speak to him, he took to his heels."

"The little savage," was all Old Clovis had to reply.

So on Christmas Eve there he is waiting for him.

A little before midnight he leaves the forge.

"If he's not at church I'll go look somewhere else, and the priest will just have to get through midnight mass without me."

Meanwhile, in the Babineaus' stable, Ti-Louis the Whistler — who has long ago exhausted his repertory of Christmas carols old and new — drags out for the third time a long . . .

Ho . . . ly . . . hic . . . *night . . . Si . . . lent . . .* hic!
and drops back into the straw under the tender and attentive gaze of the animals.

"You see," he mutters, "mustn't be sad. . . . It's Christmas . . . and besides, one day Clovis told me . . . Clovis, that's Old Clovis, my best friend . . . he told me drinking's not for guys that are sad . . . it's for guys with strong hearts, he said . . . and joyful souls. Like you and me, that's what he said . . . he said that, Old Clovis did. . . . So right now, this is no time to get all sad and sorrowful."

And with that Ti-Louis sticks his face in the straw and bawls like a baby.

The cow, the mare, and the heifers look at each other anxiously. This young man is certainly in a bad way. If only they could do something. . . .

. . . I've still got some milk left, the cow moos softly.

. . . Not us, not yet, the heifers sigh sadly.

. . . I have warm breath, interjects the mare.

At this point the sheep leaves her corner and comes closer.

. . . Baaa . . . I've got good wool, she says. And she snuggles up to the young man.

. . . I've got milk, the cow repeats, but I need someone to milk me.

At once the heifers shove their muzzles under their mother's stomach to show the young man-animal the technique.

But this festive night the man-animal has run out of strength and courage. He watches the animals' efforts to help him defeat his despair . . . thanks, he says with his eyes, thanks a lot! . . . but he doesn't move from the straw. Besides, a wave of queasiness begins to surge in the pit of his belly, a wave that rises, fills his stomach, spills into his throat and. . . .

Whoops! . . .

The animals turn away out of delicacy. Ti-Louis wipes his chin and cheeks with the back of his hand and mournfully studies his rags.

"Now you're going to stink too, Ti-Louis."

Defiantly he stares back at the cow and the mare:

"Well, so what? I'm a sad drunk like Célestine's man, like any other no-good bum of a hobo of a son of a bitch who'll never make anything of himself! I know it, you don't have to shout it so loud."

He gets up, staggers, adjusts his legs, and smiles at the animals in the stable:

"Thanks anyway . . . you did everything you could, you tried your best. . . . Well, let the others know . . . tell Clovis . . . Clovis, that's my friend . . . you tell him if he comes this way, and tell Célestine too . . . that Ti-Louis gave it a good try . . . that he tried till his heart broke."

And as he steps out into the light of the full moon, the cold strikes his face a blow and puts his head back on his shoulders.

As Clovis comes out of Long-Tongue Médard's shed he sees the Babineaus' barn standing in his path, its door banging in the wind . . . mind your own business, Clovis, barns are boot-legger territory . . . and he's about to step over the fence sticking up out of the snow under his feet when. . . . Funny thing, the Babineaus leaving their animals exposed to the night winds like that. They might at least have locked the door. . . . He goes over. The hinges creak and the cow answers. then the mare, followed by the heifers and the sheep.

"What's all this about? Are you wishing me Merry Christmas, is that it?"

And he too thinks of the legend of the animals speaking on Christmas Eve.

"Well, since that's the way it is — tell me, you wouldn't have seen a lad from the States around here . . . no, no, it doesn't matter where he comes from . . . you wouldn't have seen a lad a little small for his age, with a gap in his front teeth when he laughs . . . ? But maybe he hasn't felt much like laughing for a while."

. . . Come in, Clovis, and close the door behind you.

. . . Take a look around, Clovis. Hurry up, there's no time to lose.

. . . Look down at your feet, Clovis, and help yourself, there's a good gulp left in the bottom of the can.

"You call that a can, do you? That's a Hand Brand gallon. The best Babineau reserve, the real stuff! And by Jesus, Mary, and Joseph, somebody's already drunk half of it. Well, well! I know somebody's got woollen legs and a cotton-batton stomach tonight!"

. . . Stick your nose in the straw, old man, and you'll see what he had in his stomach, poor devil!

"Hold on a minute. Just let me try the bottom of this can. . . . Mmmm! . . . Pure Scotch whisky from Ireland, what about that! . . . Say, it's none too warm here in your stable in the middle of the night . . . yum-yum! Would you mind if I smoked a pipe to warm my fingers up a mite? . . . And by the way, Merry Christmas!"

. . . Watch out, Clovis, the straw is soaked with alcohol around here, be careful with your pipe. . . .

"Don't worry about me. Just act as if I wasn't here and go on talking."

. . . Hurry up, Clovis, the one who was through here before you was a sad drinker. Hurry up, Clovis.

"Well, if he was a sad drinker he wasn't the one I'm thinking about. . . . Unless, on Christmas Eve, all alone. . . . "

. . . Put out your pipe, old man, and take the road to the bridge.

Ti-Louis the Whistler raises his head and calculates the height of the iron bridge standing out in the moonlight. . . . Good Lord, it's high! It makes him dizzy just to look up, let alone climb it. Damn stomach! It's the whisky. But it wouldn't have dropped like molten lead into a full stomach, so you can't blame the whisky. And besides, your stomach, along with the rest of you, isn't long for this world anyway. Go

on, Ti-Louis, it's the first step that's always the hardest . . .
after that, you'll see, you'll climb up rung by rung as if there
was nothing to it . . . right up to heaven. . . . And in heaven,
Ti-Louis, there are angels and saints and a lamb of God . . .
no, those are Marie-Pet's stories. In heaven there'll be your
Ma and Pa. . . . You can be sure they'll be waiting for you. . . .
And why not? They never hurt a soul. Nor you neither,
Ti-Louis, you never hurt anybody. Never had time to. Oh,
you laughed at people a regular bellyful (your poor belly) . . .
and even when you were small you used to invent stories
that were less than half true, but that was just for laughs . . .
a man has to laugh in life. . . .That's what brought you here,
Ti-Louis . . . it's donkey's years since you had a good laugh.
You should never have left Clovis's forge . . . as for living
at Célestine's, you didn't have a chance, her man would
have kicked you out one day or another. . . . But Clovis . . .
he's the best friend heaven ever sent you in all your born
days. . . . All your born days! Why, you're talking like an old
man, Ti-Louis! You don't know what you're saying. You're
not eighteen yet! . . . but so what? . . . I figure age doesn't
count for a man who's going to kick the bucket in an hour,
his race is run anyway. An hour, Ti-Louis, it's what they call
your last hour. Well, if it's your last hour, do something
with it you'll never regret. How would you like to spend
your last hour, more than anything in the world, if you had
the choice? You do have the choice. All you've got to do is
take it. . . . They won't be able to throw you in jail for it.
They won't even hold it against you, it's not the custom
around here to hold a grudge against the dead. So don't
worry, Ti-Louis, go wherever you want . . . break into the
Babineaus', or the Robichauds', or the Dieudonnés' . . . everyone's at midnight mass. . . . You've got all the time you need
to empty their cupboards and warm your feet at their stoves.

One hour . . . it shouldn't bother anybody to see a man cram his belly full for once in his life. And even if it did bother them a little, it's Christmas. You'd eat your fill, Ti-Louis, and you'd get warmed up right to your marrowbones, that's all. Then afterwards . . . you'd tiptoe out . . . and you'd come back here and do what you have to do . . . and you'd never hear a whisper about it . . . never again. . . . But how does a man make a decision like that a second time over? After he gets up out of a soft bed, on a full stomach? Can he live a last fabulous hour and then still consent to make it his last? . . . Go on, climb up, Ti-Louis, leave the stuffing of the Babineaus' turkey crackling in its own juice. . . . Why not fill your last hour with the thing you loved the most in life . . . get out your mouth-organ and play . . . make your entry into paradise to the sound of your harmonica, Ti-Louis, and no one will turn you away, you'll see. . . . Sweet Saviour Jesus Christ! I can't climb, I can't even put my feet on the rungs, my boots are frozen to my ankles! I've got no feet left, for God's sake, nothing but boots at the ends of my legs, like horse's hoofs! Ho-ha-ha! . . . Did you hear that, Ti-Louis? Was that you laughing? . . . It was you, all right, don't try to get out of it! Holy Bejeezuz! You laughed, Ti-Louis the Whistler. And you said yourself that a man who can laugh can't take his own life. Jesus Christ, Ti-Louis, you'll remember this all your born days! A Christmas Eve when you weren't eighteen yet and your frozen boots saved your life! . . . And if you want to know what I think, my lad, it was no time to think of meeting Saint Peter anyway . . . you just swore by Christ's name three times . . . ho-ha-ha!

By now Clovis is running on the bridge . . . he has just made out a shadow framed against its iron skeleton.

"Ti-Louis!. . . Ti-Louis the Whistler!. . . " he pants. . . . Run, Clovis, you'll never run fast enough . . . shut your mouth and save your breath, but run, you rickety old codger!

And he runs.

Then suddenly he stops. No, he's not dreaming. There he is, the good-for-nothing, coming straight for him with his music-maker in his jaws, Ti-Louis himself in flesh and blood, smiling, laughing, dancing, and playing the *Te Deum* to a jig tune. Clovis grabs him, hugs him, smothers him, and shouts at the top of his lungs,

"What's the idea, scaring me like that, you little bugger! Don't you know you might have been the death of me?"

"Ho-ha-ha! No way, Clovis. A man who can laugh isn't ready to die. Remember that all your born days. As long as your shoulders are shaking, the grim reaper will stay away from your bedside."

And stumping along, hanging on to Ti-Louis's arm, Old Clovis reflects that this youngster has picked up a good deal of wisdom for one night.

It is two knights of the Order of the Evening Star whom Crache-à-Pic finally catches up with at the downramp of the bridge. At almost the last instant she had the same presentiment as Old Clovis and rushed off to the bridge, outdistancing the two cousins who came puffing after. When all the rescuers were at last reunited, in a single pile of wool and furs and laughter and shouts of joy, the first sentence to emerge complete with a subject and verb from one of their mouths came from Clovis:

"I'm hungry," he said. "Come on over to the forge and we'll have pancakes for our *réveillon*."

But Tobie was pulling at his sister's coat.

"Crache-à-Pic! Crache-à-Pic!"

Then Crache-à-Pic saw the flames.

"The Babineaus' barn is on fire!"

Clovis let out a "Holy Moses! My pipe!" and then tried to swallow it back again. But at this juncture nobody was paying any attention to Old Clovis's ramblings. Ti-Louis stared wide-eyed. Then his memory revived and he thought of the animals.

"The cow and the mare!" he cried out. "We can't leave them there. And the sheep and the heifers, too. . . . "

"The Babineaus' animals!" Céleste grumbled. "Those Babineaus have got plenty to buy others with, don't you go risking your lives."

But Ti-Louis wasn't thinking of the Babineaus. He was thinking of the animals he'd spent his last hour with, and he dove into the flames. The Twins joined him, then Crache-à-Pic and Jimmy-the-Flea. Céleste and Célestine threw their arms around Tobie and held him back with all their might.

"They won't burn, Tobie . . . not the animals or the people . . . they'll be all right, they won't burn."

It was nearly two in the morning when the double doors of the church opened to spill the crowd of worshippers out into the bright Christmas night. Doubly bright: the light of the full moon frolicked with the most splendid fireworks display the coast had ever seen. Sparks burst into the air like skyrockets. You'd have thought the devil himself was fanning the flames.

And while the whole of Sainte-Marie-des-Côtes stood on the church steps, admiring the spectacle and laughing to themselves to hear the gallons of Hand Brand exploding into the stars, the Babineaus tried to sneak off, their faces hidden in their furs. The secret they had so carefully kept buried under the hay of their barn during their most prosperous years was now blazing into the night sky in a joyous show of pyrotechnics.

"It's the dance of the will-o'-the-wisps," roared Xavier-the-Hunchback.

"No such thing, it's the star of Bethlehem blown up to kingdom come," Melchior, king of the Three Kings, corrected him.

Others suggested that now the Babineaus were really on the hot seat. Everyone agreed on one point:

"There'll be a lot of thirsty throats tomorrow!"

Next day Old Clovis, Ti-Louis, Jimmy-the-Flea, and the Twins received a gift of turkeys and chicken stew from the Babineaus, for having saved the animals at the risk of their lives.

"That was a fine Christmas!" said Ti-Louis. "A damn fine Christmas!"

She was watching the orphan crunch his chicken bones when Crache-à-Pic came up with her idea.

"Did Dieudonné keep on making money out of his gramophones this year?" she asked, not looking at anyone in particular.

The gramophone was the latest fad on the coast. People would go into debt or prostitution, or sell their shirts, for a wind-up gramophone. They would even mortgage their property. Once again Dieudonné had made a shrewd guess. He knew how to kill two birds with one stone, all right; the gramophones served as both bait and camouflage. At the end of the line flopped the barns, sheds, and fields of the poor devils on the coast. Dieudonné was born and bred in these parts; he knew that the hungrier you are, the more your foot goes tapping. With his gramophone scheme he had everyone dancing to his tune.

Long after the Depression, Old Clovis felt bound to admit to my father that, with all due respect, Dieudonné hadn't been such a sly fox as usual in this gramophone business.

"No sirree! In the gramophone affair big Dieudonné met his match."

And his match was the people of the coast.

"You see," said the old storyteller. . . .

And he went on to say that you shouldn't push a man to the limit. For when the poor starving devils caught on to the fact that they were going to be skinned to the bone and then swallowed whole, they sat down in a circle round the lamp one fine evening and put their heads together.

"Nothing worse for the bigwigs than when the small fry get together and begin to plot," Old Clovis confided.

They plotted so well that in the end they found a way out. With a little good will and a strong arm to turn the crank, a gramophone with a big resonating box could be heard from Cocagne to Champdoré. So why not gather, now at one person's home, now at another's, and let the rest of the country go on cultivating their fields in peace? That way no one need fear seeing Dieudonné's men coming, papers in hand, to seize their property.

They claim the idea was conceived in old centenarian Ozite's rocking-chair.

. . . First it's the Allains who buy one on credit for a month, let's say January. At the end of the month, since they can't pay, it's confiscated. Now, since Dieudonné is nobody's fool, he sells the Allains' gramophone to the Collettes, who invite everyone to come over and warm up their feet to La Bolduc's tunes, through the February storms. New confiscation at the end of the month, resale to the LeBlancs in March, in April to the Légers, in May to the Caissies . . . no, not the Caissies, Marie-Pet doesn't dance . . . to the Maillets, who spend a merry month of May. You'll never get me to believe that the country can't provide enough respectable homes to keep the handle of the gramophone turning twelve months a year!

So the only one who paid was Dieudonné, while the poor kept tapping their feet all year long! Oh, the sly dogs! Sly and then some!

And Old Clovis had a coughing fit that almost carried him off.

Dieudonné's eyes were eventually opened the day he got his nose pinched between two columns in his account book. He was balancing receipts and expenses the last day of the year when he suddenly slammed the big book shut and closed down the gramophone business. The whole country was chewing its nails. Right in the middle of the holiday season, too! Empty stomachs and no music. Not quite empty, no, for Crache-à-Pic had secretly sworn she'd quench the coast's thirst from the bootleggers' stores. And when someone's capable of seizing the president's wines and cognac at night, on the open sea, in a raging nor'easter . . . well, you don't have to worry about the rum and the whisky. But there was still this question of the music.

"Shine up your mouth-organ, Ti-Louis, and shake out your shanks. You're going to spend the holidays making the country dance."

He spent all winter at it.

Old Clovis took it upon himself to introduce him to

the Goguens of Cocagne on New Year's Eve. The Goguens raised geese, and Clovis guessed that their biggest gander would finish the year off roasting in his own grease. He suggested they cheer on the occasion with some music.

"It won't cost you any more than the bones of the bird," he said.

And that night Ti-Louis ate his fill.

Next day all Cocagne were treating their feet for blisters and hanging out their hangovers. Which made Grand-Digue laugh at them for not knowing how to drink or dance. Then, in secret, Grand-Digue sent a messenger to the forge to reserve the Whistler for Twelfth Night. But Village-des-Trois-Maisons had already taken the precaution of warning Champdoré to send word to Bois-Joli to the effect that Sainte-Marie-des-Côtes was likely to end up in the last pew, like the eldest daughter who lets her younger sister get married first, right under her nose.

No sir! Not that!

So Sainte-Marie-des-Côtes had its very own Ti-Louis for Twelfth Night. A Ti-Louis who played the harmonica, stamped his foot, whistled, and sang — sang ten different songs and then came back to the first ones all over again, adding couplets, improvising, transposing, fol-de-roling, dancing, prancing, and dropping from exhaustion. Whereupon the women busied themselves around this poor child of the Good Lord, rubbing his ankles and the back of his neck, feeding him up . . . just take another piece, Ti-Louis . . . and finally getting him back on his feet again. At dawn the musician made his way back to Clovis's forge, dead beat but happy as a king.

And the next day it began all over again.

It was Clovis himself who made his report to Crache-à-Pic: Ti-Louis was eating his fill and Dieudonné had closed his gramophone store.

Just the same, the winter of 1931 was one of the hardest the coast had ever known. Two of the seven plagues of Egypt struck the country: cold and famine.

. . . Plagues of Egypt! Famine I'll grant you, but cold, Clovis? Cold in Egypt?

By the time mid-Lent rolled around Ti-Louis couldn't think what more music to invent in order to extract another mouthful of bread from his hosts. The partygoers were often so hungry themselves they forgot to feed the musician.

Afterwards he confessed to Old Clovis,

"I played to unfreeze my fingers, stomped my feet to warm up my legs, and sang so I wouldn't hear my gut rumbling. That saw me through part of the night. Once I even nearly croaked, and people thought I was playing a lament. Next day Jeannette asked for a repeat performance."

Hee-hee-hee!

. . . One day, said Old Clovis, this scamp of a Ti-Louis found an egg in the presbytery henhouse . . . an egg that had been overlooked and would have gone rotten. Better take it along home, he said to himself. Times being what they are, nobody likes to waste food. So he brought it to the forge to share with Clovis. Share an egg? Did you ever hear the like? An apple maybe, and an acorn perhaps, but an egg? So Clovis urged him to eat the egg all by himself. But the kid was stubborn as a mule. Both or nobody, he says. So Clovis replied, if that's it, then nobody. And the egg stayed there, rolling around on the table between the cracks. You know, Clovis finally said, if it's for nobody, might as well get rid of it right now. And Ti-Louis agreed: Right now. So Old Clovis got up, warmed the egg tenderly in his palm, and said to Ti-Louis:

One, two, three, let her go! Ti-Louis didn't budge so the old boy heaved back and threw the egg into the fireplace, where in no time flat it made an omelet.

"At least," concluded Clovis, "we could share the smell of fried egg, which was mighty sweet to our nostrils."

Certain families had a harder time of it than others. Xavier-the-Hunchback claimed his wife hung a piece of pork rind up over the frying-pan. In the heat of the fire the fat slowly melted and dripped into the pan, and at mealtimes the famished children had permission to wipe the pan with a crust of bread.

"You were lucky your wife had a piece of pork rind," Melchior put in. "Over at our place it was my sock we used to hang over the frying-pan."

And everyone broke up laughing.

So this was the way Ti-Louis got through the winter and managed, along with everyone else, to make it into spring by the front door.

"Ah yes! By the front door all right," Old Clovis insisted.

The first one to drag himself out of winter was Tobie's bear. It was Céleste who first saw him, coming up from under the apple tree like a ghost, stretching his legs, sniffing the air, and growling. She had just poured a basin of wash water into the ditch in her back yard and was on the point of going in again when she saw the roots of the apple tree stirring and the bear's head come up. "I'm a goner," she said to herself. "I've as good as measured out my length in the ground." Then she thought to remind the bear of her relationship to the Crache-à-Pics. "It's me, Céleste," she shouted at him. "I'm one of the family. . . ." But he didn't seem much impressed and came straight at her. Naturally the bear was hungry; Céleste had just thrown her dirty water into the stream; the field was completely bare; she was the only edible thing on the scene.

She took up her wash basin and used it as a shield, challenging the bear to attack if he dared.

He dared . . . but he took care to go round Céleste and her basin and grab her in a bear-hug from behind. There they were like a couple of springtime lovers when Tobie ran up shouting, "Bear! Bear!" and threw his arms around the bear's neck. The bear didn't resist, and let himself be led off gently to the door of the barn where Tobie had hidden a store of acorns and hazelnuts.

"Eat," he said. "And don't be afraid of Céleste, she won't hurt you."

Meanwhile Céleste had reorganized her hair-bun and gone off to find Crache-à-Pic, cursing humanity in general and the bear in particular as a bunch of worthless good-for-nothings. And it was decided by neighbourhood decree that from that day forward the bear would be tied up to the apple tree, and that no one but Tobie would go near him.

"He should serve as a fair-to-middling watchdog," added Crache-à-Pic.

Even tied up, the bear kept any ill-intentioned marauders away from Cap-Lumière. . . . The Twins wondered what Crache-à-Pic could be worried about — she who had never been afraid of a thing in her life — but they kept this reflection to themselves, and settled for a solemn shake of the head.

One April morning Ti-Louis the Whistler saw Melchior and his two poaching pals approaching at a run.

"We've got company," he said to Clovis, as the company kicked the door open and piled in.

"The devil is loose!"

And all three began talking at once.

. . . In the old presbytery . . . the retreat house. . . .

"Now what's up? A brand new ghost?"

"Better than that, Clovis, much better than any old ghost. The bootleggers' chief hiding-place! In the old retreat house! The stuff was everywhere. And it's not even the officers who found it."

"Holy smokes! Who's the lucky one? Not Long-Tongue Médard by any chance?"

"Not a chance, not him — everyone would have known the very first day. No, it's the Twins! They must have spent a mighty fine winter over at Cap-Lumière."

"No way," chipped in Balthazar. "I'll bet they went and hid the stuff all over again, and one of these days Crache-à-Pic's gang is going to spring a surprise on us."

"Anyway, in the meantime Dieudonné's mad as a bull to find his cache empty, and the *curé* is angry as a bear at thinking about what his building was full of all winter."

Everyone agreed on one point: the sermons on Sundays to come would not be preached on the subject of the apocryphal gospels.

Old Clovis wanted to know the details: What kind of Hand Brand? How many cases? And who had spilled the beans on the Twins?

. . . That was still a mystery. Someone had talked. Certain people thought it was the Babineaus . . . on account of because the Babineaus had heard say recently that their barn might not have burned down due to what you might call natural causes. And they had thought of the Twins.

"Why the Twins?" Clovis asked quickly.

"Why not? They were around at the time of the fire. Like you. But the Babineaus would hardly go accusing you of setting fire to their barn, would they? Proud as peacocks and greedy as vultures the Babineaus may be, but they're not completely nuts."

Old Clovis went over to the hearth to knock out his pipe.

"The first one who goes accusing the Twins of setting fire to that barn will have to deal with me," he said, in a tone that left the three poachers perplexed.

Curé Ouellet's sermon the following Sunday did not disappoint the parish. As Clovis put it, without pointing at anyone he spelt out the names and gave graphic descriptions of the heathens who had pushed sacrilege so far as to trample the most sacred things. Alcoholic beverages in a religious retreat house! The priest lost his voice in indignation. Climbing down from the pulpit he even lost his biretta, a brand new biretta which rolled right down to the front pew where Dieudonné's wife sat, freshly dishonoured. She would never forgive her husband such a blunder. To cast the gates of scandal wide open to every wind that blows! It almost suffocated her. In a rage she picked up the priest's hat and threw it at the nearest choirboy, who got it right in the stomach like a football. The ceremony was turning sour. It was high time to let off some steam. So Dieudonné's wife, followed by her daughters, marched out the main aisle just as the whole parish rose for the *Credo*.

Dieudonné had no choice. Some time later he paid the priest a visit.

After their embarrassment on the bay the bootleggers had had the whole winter to bargain with stolen car dealers, who had turned up again right after Santa Claus's departure. And by the time the wild geese came back, Buicks, Fords, Marmons, Oldsmobiles, Lincolns, and Cadillacs, all newly released from the Montréal marshalling yards — by night — were to be seen negotiating the coastal roads again.

The Cadillac, as was fitting, fell to Dieudonné for his personal use. And it was in this new *Mae West*, all upholstered in gold plush, that the bootlegger drove up to the presbytery door one May morning.

"Month of Mary, month of reconciliations!" as he said to the priest.

He had come, without ceremony but with dignity, to pardon the Church for its malicious insinuations which had so disturbed his wife — women are so sensitive — and to offer a handshake of forgiveness to the completely dumbfounded Abbé Ouellet.

"But . . . but. . . ."

But the priest had no time to reply or correct Dieudonné who, while presenting the olive branch with one hand, gestured with the other towards his brand new automobile — just the thing, surely, to take a priest along the highways and byways of the United States to visit his family relations down there for a week or two.

"You, you mean to say . . . ?"

Why, yes, Father, that's it exactly.

So, for all the bad names evil tongues were wont to attribute to him, Dieudonné in person lent the *curé* his Cadillac, not even broken in yet, not even five thousand miles on it, barely out of the factory, a Cadillac that would certainly be able to find its own way back to the States without any trouble.

"Go in peace, Father. If anyone in Sainte-Marie-des-Côtes deserves a holiday, it's you! And I'm afraid, no offence meant, that your Model T wouldn't make it as far as the border."

"Ah! As far as that goes, you're right, Dieudonné. But a priest is at the service of God and his parish. Soon it will be the Feast of Rogations, and then. . . ."

"And then Ascension, then Corpus Christi, then Saint Anne's Day. . . . The Church has strewn its Holy Days throughout the year to prevent its priests from burning the candle at both ends. That is why not a few of them end their days in the hospital."

Abbé Ouellet blinked in astonishment. What a man, this Dieudonné! And one who could recite the liturgical feasts in order without even consulting the calendar. Could it be he wasn't as much of a heathen as people said? Yet old Father Belliveau wasn't one to talk just for the sake of talking. . . .

As if Dieudonné had been reading the priest's thoughts, he interrupted them in mid-stream:

"Why don't you take Father Belliveau along with you? He has a brother getting on in years who lives in Massachusetts, from what I hear."

The priest's servant never listened at the office door; the *curé*'s office was like the confessional. And if there was a Catholic on the coast who knew her religious duties, after Marie-Pet, it was Annie from the presbytery. But this exceptional visit was taking place in the parlour. That changed everything.

Next day the whole parish learned that its *curé* was taking a holiday in the States and wouldn't be in Sainte-Marie-des-Côtes for Rogation Week. But they were not to worry, everything had been looked after. Priests from Cocagne and Grand-Digue would share replacement duties, so Sainte-Marie would not go without a holy hand to bless the seed before it was planted in the earth. A few sour notes, however, came squeaking up from the marsh hay and the bull-rushes: Did a priest have the right to up and abandon his flock like that? . . . And did a priest have the right to a vaca-tion anyway, when none of the unemployed in the country could afford to take one? . . . And besides, what got into him to take off in a Cadillac, of all things?

. . . Shut up, you Communists!

He had just succumbed to a sudden appetite for free-dom and adventure, that was all, the appetite of a poor boy who had only seen his first automobile when he was ten, and hadn't sat behind the wheel till he was forty. And here he was now, being offered two weeks' use of a brand new Cadillac in black and gold, practically the colours of the Church. . . .

". . . the colours of the *De Profundis* at somebody's funeral," wisecracked one old reprobate from a corner of the forge.

Abbé Ouellet had tried to resist, sprinkling his inter-nal debate with signs of the cross and O-my-God-come-to-my-aid's. But the final argument — the devil's last card, he was to call it later — was Dieudonné's show of humility in lower-ing himself to the point of offering to do his own business in the priest's four-pedal Model T while Abbé Ouellet rode around in the Cadillac. What's good enough for a *curé* is good enough for his parishioner, Dieudonné said.

"For a couple of weeks it won't kill me."

Despite the fact that Abbé Ouellet left the presbytery by the back door, on tiptoe, at five in the morning, his par-ish was there waiting for him. Marie-Pet with a freshly baked sugar pie; Malvina with a johnny-cake; the doctor's chil-dren with a bouquet of mayflowers; the Three Kings push-ing forward Old Clovis, who was pushing a wheelbarrow full of hay with such an innocent air that everyone doubted that the hay was meant to feed a ten-horsepower automobile. The *curé* stuck his hand under the hay and frowned:

"Thanks anyway, Clovis," he said, "but I'm not going to the States to get myself arrested at the border."

And he handed back the old man's jug of *whisky blanc*.

Finally along came Clovis's daughter-in-law, Jeannette, offering a kettle full of dumplings floating in gravy. The *curé* wondered how he was going to balance this cauldron filled to the brim with gluey stew on the plush seat of the Cadillac.

. . . You'd really have to be starving to take along something like that, grumbled Clovis, shooting a dark look at his son's wife. His daughter Agnès would never have offered the priest such a poisoned present.

His daughter Agnès offered her *curé* a branch of apple blossom to plant in American soil. Father Ouellet transplanted it into a ditch on the outskirts of Village-des-Trois-Maisons to free the front seat and leave a little room for Father Belliveau, who came dragging along behind him a parish every bit as generous as Sainte-Marie-des-Côtes.

When the two *curés* finally took the road to the south, laden down with tenderness, they looked like a couple of prospectors setting out for the Klondike.

Without his biretta, which never left his head except when he was asleep but which now reposed on top of a pile of crates, suitcases, sewing-kits, first-aid boxes, pots, pans, spare tires, fishing-rods, and photo-albums sent by the Bourques to show to their relatives in Lowell, Mass. . . . without his hat the *curé* looked quite different, and the villages of Champdoré, Cocagne, or Grand-Digue would have been hard-pressed to recognize either of their neighbouring priests. So it was not until a day or two later that the news reached the ears of Constable Martial, who transmitted it to the Royal

Canadian Mounted Police, who telegraphed it to the border.

Martial had all the rest of his life to deplore his excessive zeal, and that of the American customs officers. For when it came to smuggling liquor, the Americans were much stickier than their neighbours to the north, especially because it was their Congress that had voted in Prohibition in the first place, and then kept it on the books. So the officers of the U.S. coastguard often reproached their Canadian counterparts for their slackness.

It was therefore decided in high places to make an example of the Canadians, an example all the more telling because it touched the Maritime provinces in their two most powerful institutions: rum-running and the Roman Catholic Church.

And to think what a beautiful trip it had been till then! Not a flat, not a drop of rain, not even a herd of cows on the road to slow their progress — twenty miles an hour on the average, and that's no lie. Everything had been running so smoothly. And then our two *curés* from the coast quite innocently ran smack into the "Stop! In the name of the law!" of half a dozen customs officers who were in no mood to trifle with either contraband or religion, that day.

. . . And it's dressing up as priests now, is it? Is there no shame then? And to be taking us Americans for a bunch of choirboys! No shame there, either! . . .

Oh yes, there was shame all right. Shame enough to make them feel like doing it right in their soutanes. And even more shame when the customs men made the false priests strip right down . . . get them searched, and step on it! . . . take off everything, their shirts, their underwear . . . oh my! . . . and prove, once they were as naked as rats, that they knew how to sing High Mass.

Lucky for the American customs that it was several

weeks before Sainte-Marie-des-Côtes and Village-des-Trois-Maisons learnt about the treatment their *curés* had received. Lucky for those Irish Catholic officers that they belonged to an American diocese, the heretics, because there were grounds here for excommunication! Even Clovis and his gang of old foxes, who always arrived late at mass, took the sacrilegious insult the customs had paid their Church very badly.

Yet the poor customs men hadn't prolonged the search beyond the limits set by law and practice. Everyone got stripped down in those days if they didn't seem Catholic enough.

. . . Not enough, or too much.

For that matter they searched the Cadillac even more thoroughly than the passengers. They let the air out of its tires, knifed open the seats, emptied the gas tank, and were just thinking about going into the motor when the head customs officer heard one of his prisoners, naked as Christ Jesus on the Cross, singing the *Preface* to High Mass in Latin.

Of all the Irish Catholics in America, Officer McFadden was the most Catholic and the most Irish. He grabbed the handiest customs man by the neck and shook him so roundly that his fleas took off in a panic for the Canadian side of the border.

So Clovis says.

While the drama of the two *curés* was being played out at the frontier — a drama that drew forth so many apologies and gifts from the American officials, after the priests' rehabilitation, that the *curés* decided to continue their trip and visit their relatives anyway — back home the other side of the comedy was being staged. Every day one of the Damien boys, or Little Philias, or sometimes Black Willy himself, would take Abbé Ouellet's Model T out for a spin just to break it in.

"Break it in at 200,000 miles!" laughed the whole country, seeing the four-pedal Ford pop up at the most unusual times and places.

Some old folks in the back country, not up on the bootleggers' latest fantasies, would kneel in the fields seeing the ecclesiastical vehicle approaching with its sacraments for the sick. They would even cross themselves, heads bowed, as Black Willy bombed along bringing the sick a little pick-me-up before the last rites.

One morning Dieudonné sent for his right-hand man. He was in high spirits, bubbling over with fresh ideas, each more ingenious than the last. For one thing, his strategy had worked; first Martial, then the American officers had been taken in completely. At the frontier they had arrested two real priests as impostors; next week they wouldn't be so quick to arrest a false lobster salesman as the real thing.

His boss was in such good humour that Black Willy didn't dare raise objections about lobster fished outside territorial waters, by poachers we've already met.

"I could just as well send you over selling gramophones or sewing machines."

But — besides the fact that the States produced a hundred times more sewing machines than Canada, and lived under a rigorous protectionist regime — sewing machines or gramophones looked so innocent they would immediately arouse suspicion. Whereas lobsters. . . . But it was up to the fisheries officers to distinguish between lobsters from the north and lobsters from the south, explained Dieudonné. So as far as customs was concerned it would just be: Okay! Next!

"And you'll pass through slick as a whistle, and you can go sell your lobsters to Al Capone's men."

Black Willy jumped. The great Al Capone and Legs Diamond, his idols! At last he was going to draw near the sanctuary of contraband — he, Black Willy, the little guy from the coast born in a smelt-fishing shack! Saliva swelled his cheeks. He wanted to know everything about his mission, down to the last detail . . . the ice that would keep the lobsters fresh, and would at the same time cool the two-and-a-half-gallon cans of over-proof alcohol marked with the sign of the Hand. He would be driving a two-ton truck and would have only one man with him: the giant Joe Colossus, for his general appearance and his gigantic virtues.

"Joe can change a tire for you by just putting his shoulder under the chassis," said Dieudonné. "And besides, a giant will frighten off any little scum prowling around at night. There's just one thing, don't let him open his mouth; nobody but you does the talking when you're crossing the border."

All that was left for Black Willy to do before D-Day was move the cans of hooch from the hideaway to the truck. It was child's play. He used his best men and horses for the job, at night, taking care to wrap a piece of cloth around each axle before fixing the wheel back on again. Absolutely no squeaking! Every horse was fitted out with a feed-bag to stifle the sound of its whinnying. And to cut down the noise from the stones on the road, they tied rags around the horses' hoofs. As for the men . . . well, the men were used to it — and they wouldn't be paid until the job was done.

"Five bucks a night if they brought it off," Clovis asserted. "But when the schooner didn't show up, or the officers did, a guy could lie there flat on his belly in the swamp until dawn, shivering all he liked, and nothing left for him to do next morning but go beg a bowl of soup from his mother. That was the law of rum-running. There was no gainsaying it. And who was there to bitch to anyway, eh?"

Crache-à-Pic.

More and more the hired hands — the second- and third-hand ones, who never got a glimpse of the big boss but were hired by the day, by the underling of an underling — more and more men of that breed had been seen prowling around Cap-Lumière lately. The Three Kings wondered if the idea was to lay a trap for Crache-à-Pic, or to make a deal with her. After all, the retreat house couldn't have been rifled that winter without inside information and willing hands to do the work.

But in preparing his big job for the States, the job leading right up to Al Capone's doorstep, Dieudonné didn't have time to waste on the little bitch from Cap-Lumière. Like all victims of the Depression Crache-à-Pic had spent a bad winter; she was now floating around in her skirt and probably didn't have enough spunk left to outfit herself again anyway, so. . . .

Black Willy didn't understand it, he just couldn't understand it at all. Who, what, how? What son of a bitch of a gossiping busybody had spilled the beans?

Yet he had left Sainte-Marie-des-Côtes as planned, by night, behind the wheel of a truck bought new this spring — from a legitimate dealer this time, so as to leave nothing to chance; a truck with proper papers and plates, clean, pure, as virgin as a first communion.

"Stop! In the name of the law!"

But poor Black Willy didn't know how to sing the

Preface in Latin. He'd even forgotten how to recite his Act of Contrition in French, though he was badly in need of it. For on seeing the American officers make a beeline for the gallons of alcohol sitting pretty under the ice, like so many winter oysters, he felt his last hour had come. Dieudonné had given him one last chance. But for a year now Lady Luck hadn't been smiling on Black Willy, or on his boss either. For a year now he'd been driving around on square wheels. From the depths of his desperate thoughts he heard one of the customs officers swearing like the devil:

"Goddam little nuns!" he was yelling.

And through the thick mist fogging his brain, the chief bootlegger's right-hand man saw it all in a flash: Crache-à-Pic!

She had planned her stunt carefully, the little slut! Once again she had simply walked in Dieudonné's footsteps. Didn't try to get ahead of him, did nothing more than follow his tracks — but placing her feet between them, to confuse the scent better. A real foxtrot! Dieudonné didn't have any choice left: it was him or her. Either he sent her to the bottom of the sea, or she'd send him to hell in a handcart.

As for Black Willy — trying to swallow his rage, he swore and sputtered, and hurled curses at the customs officers and threats at Joe Colossus, who shifted from one foot to the other hardly knowing which to put his giant's weight on. They had charged him to hold his tongue and he was holding it. But that didn't stop him from making faces like a gorilla in a cage.

"I'll kill her! I'll kill her!" raged Black Willy, seeing the lobsters, freed from their bed of ice, regaining consciousness and squirming around in the back of the truck.

While their superiors busied themselves with the Hand Brand and looked the other way, two young officers were already stuffing the largest specimens into burlap bags under the goggling eyes of Joe Colossus, who had sworn to Dieu-donné not to open his mouth at the border.

"I'll clobber her with a pick-axe, the damned witch!" Black Willy bellowed.

Finally his nose started to bleed, as it did every time he lost control of his violent temper. The nosebleed calmed him down and obliged him to lean forward, his head in his hands, over the gutter. The customs officers abandoned him to his misery, too eager to unload and label their precious haul to change handkerchiefs for a jailbird with a bloody nose. An hour later, however, when they went to turn their bird over to police who'd come from the nearest town, they had to settle for Joe Colossus; having rid himself of his bad blood at the border, Black Willy had taken to the woods.

Ironically, it was in a Maine convent — where he shared the hospitality with some of the numerous vagabonds who filled the roads during the Depression — that Black Willy heard the story of an extraordinary odyssey, told by one of those loose-tongued down-and-outers who were legion in those days. A newly minted odyssey, not yet worn into leg-end; the odyssey of a certain Reverend Sister Marie of the Holy Spittle of the Child Jesus, and her companion, Sister Marie of the Celestial Stars.

"The what?!!"

In the poorhouse barn where the Sisters sent the hobos to sleep, Black Willy had no need of a disguise to pass incog-nito. He blended in with the cast of snooper-prowler-broke-and-homeless like a pea in the soup. He was dossed down between a wall-eye and a harelip when he heard this fancy-talker, who proudly went by the name of Barabbas, praising the merits of Reverend Marie of the Holy Spittle.

The name made Black Willy bounce up like a spring.

"What's that you said?"

So Barabbas, red-faced with hooch, good humour, and inspiration, took up his story from the beginning again for the benefit of his new admirer.

. . . He wasn't one to open his mouth without good cause, this Barabbas wasn't, only in order to philosophize, eat, or breathe. In that order. Times were bad enough already without purposely making them worse — by anything as futile as work, for example. Certain of his friends of the open road, among them that fine fellow The Holy Soak, made it a point of honour to spend an hour or so looking for work every Monday morning. Bah! Cat mush! Barabbas watched them leave hangdog and come back happy, having wasted sixty precious minutes of their lives every week. What a shame! That was just how crazy zealots in the past had missed the flight of comets.

Black Willy squirmed and scratched his fleabites. Raging inwardly. Get to the point, Barabbas, what about the story of those Sisters . . . Holy Spittle and Celestial Stars. . . .

He was getting there. At his own speed. Two comets, a young one and an old one, had burst into the barn just after Matins, that hour when normal people are snoring, animals are beginning to stir, and Sisters are praying. These two mustn't have been expecting to find a living soul in the barn, because they were laughing under their veils like a couple of novices in the sacristy.

"Two nunnies they were, my good sir! Oh yes, two nunnies black and white from head to toe. And believe me, I saw their underskirts and all, black too, yes indeed!"

. . . He had seen many curious things in his short life, Barabbas had: elephants in Central Park, calves with five legs, Niagara Falls, the cathedral at Cap-de-la-Madeleine, the dwarfs' house in Montréal, a half-ton turtle, and Halley's Comet. But he never imagined that one day he'd see a nunny doing a striptease . . . two nunnies, one young and one old. Not so old either . . . fifty maybe. Still quite appetizing, as far as that goes. But the young one! Holy Father in Heaven! A real fairy, that one! As nicely curved as if she'd been shaped with a knife, skin as soft as a lace window-curtain — a regular saint she was, fit to put on a scapular medal!

And Barabbas licked his chops at the thought, while Black Willy's eyes boggled.

. . . And laughing fit to kill under their veils, and choking up singing:

You take my crown

It is your own!

. . . and slapping their thighs and smacking each other on the back and rolling around in the straw and . . . and at that very instant what should come practically rolling right into the barn but a rumble-seat Model T driven by a schoolboy.

"I don't know where the kid learned to drive, but he made that buggy run forward in reverse and then backwards front-end foremost. And all the while he was playing with the steering wheel, he never quit playing the mouth-organ as loud as you please."

" . . . Ti-Louis the Whistler," muttered Black Willy.

"What's that you say?" asked Barabbas.

But he didn't wait for an answer; he went right on with this beautiful true story that life had handed him on a silver platter, just the day before.

"Now don't you go trying to tell me I've never seen nothing, or never heard the angels sing!"

. . . Angels, yessir, stripping right down, veil, skirt, petticoats, coif, the whole shebang, off with it! Then all of a sudden they notice you lying there in the hay, and they look at you, and size you up, and take your measure, and finally come over and sit down beside you and tell you everything. First their names: Sister Marie of the Celestial Stars — how do you do, Sister — and Sister Marie of the Holy Spittle of the Child Jesus — pleased to meet you! Seems they've just spent the night in the convent, received there with full honours by the Mother Superior herself who showed them their cells, with a bed, white sheets, a wash basin, holy pictures, Palm Sunday fronds, and a bottle of holy water each to sprinkle themselves with to chase off demons before they went to sleep. And it seems Sister Celestial Stars was so thirsty she drank half of hers, and found it tasted like Holy Saturday . . . a wee bit rancid.

. . . And the two of them together told Barabbas the story of their adventures, as well as the story of the story they told the Mother Superior, to the effect that they were two Canadian nunnies out collecting for the missions.

. . . Collecting in the States? the Mother Superior wanted to know.

. . . For the little Chinese in Africa, said Sister Marie of the Celestial Stars.

. . . And it seems the Mother Superior swallowed it whole.

Black Willy feels the bile oozing out of the glands in his liver.

"And the Superior believed that!" he roars at Barabbas.

But Barabbas doesn't like to be interrupted when he's got a head of steam up. So he simply raises two fingers of his right hand, like a bishop, and carries on.

. . . You see, these two nunnies had found their vocations when they found their habits, two of the Sisters' habits hanging on a nail inside the porch of the convent . . . just by chance. I mean they found them by chance. Because as long as the fine weather lasted the Sister-gardeners used to change from their farm-habits into their church-habits right there at the back porch, so they wouldn't come in to sing Vespers smelling of the stable. So one fine day our two travellers, who had to cross the line without being recognized, had the great idea of passing themselves off as a couple of nun-nies, so they said, on account of how customs had arrested two real priests just the day before, taking them for false ones, so that. . . .

It's Black Willy who finishes the sentence, modelling it on Dieudonné's bright idea.

" . . . next day they'd likely raise their eyes to heaven and let two phony Sisters cross over as real ones."

And he clenches his teeth.

She would have to go slipping in between the two, the bitch, between the priests and the lobster salesman, and at the same stroke unmask Black Willy and throw him, with his usual bad luck, straight to the wolves.

Seeing the newcomer so crestfallen and apparently taking no pleasure in the story, Barabbas fishes around in his rags and pulls out a little sealed flask which he swore he'd keep for a special occasion.

"A present from the Catholic Church to Barabbas," he says, passing it over to Black Willy — who can't suppress a smile, despite his rage.

"You don't know how right you are, my friend. This whisky even spent part of the winter in a retreat house."

And he takes a gulp of the reserve his boss intended for Al Capone's men.

Seeing his guest's thirst, Barabbas says anxiously,

"Those nunnies warned me to make it last. On account of because they were going to deliver their load down Boston way, and on the way back they wouldn't have any left."

Black Willy seizes the words out of the air.

"They're coming back this way?" he asks offhandedly.

"In two or three days at the outside. It's me they told to keep their clothes for them."

Three days later Barabbas hears a motor in the distance and recognizes the rumble-seat Model T.

"Hey, come and see!" he calls, "The nunnies are back."

But Black Willy doesn't come foward; he stays crouched in his nest of hay.

The Ford makes a long detour to approach the convent barn from behind, running over haycocks and broken fence-gates on the way. Ti-Louis the Whistler has learned to drive in two days, specially for this expedition. He was chosen because he knew the country, and spoke the language better than Jimmy-the-Flea, who garbled it, or the Twins, who even garbled their own language. He's beginning to develop a taste for his new job as chauffeur-interpreter-valet for a congregation of contraband nuns.

The congregation steps down from the car and strides into the haybarn as if they own it. Seeing his friend rise up out of the hay, Barabbas opens his mouth to make the introductions — but he's cut short by a cry from Sister Celestial Stars.

"Jesus, Mary, and Joseph! What's that varmint doing in our path?"

Black Willy, streaked with dust and speared with straw, has his moment of triumph.

"He's here to block it for you, you sons of bitches!"

Crache-à-Pic takes a deep breath and casts an eye around her; then, pushing Céleste and Barabbas out of the way, she advances right under the enemy's nose.

"Well, Black Willy, looks to me as if you'd lost some weight since last week. What's the matter, not getting your fill in the convent barns? I can get you invited to the Sisters' table if you like."

Black Willy restrains himself from wringing her neck. After all, she can't get away from him now. Two women and an adolescent barely out of short pants, caught in a barn in the act of bootlegging, plus theft of nuns' garments, plus use of false identities . . . just wait till the Mother Superior finds out who she's been providing with holy water to fight off demons!

Crache-à-Pic meets his bloodshot stare without flinching. She's seen others before.

. . . Is that so? Other traps as good as this one? This she-devil may be a specialist in tricks, but she's probably never foreseen the day she'd fall into a trap herself.

. . . A trap? What trap? She has just come by, quiet as you please, to put on her habit so she can quietly go and eat and sleep in the convent and leave next day, she and Céleste and Ti-Louis the Whistler, to quietly cross the border. . . .

"Aha! So, my fine little bitch, you think I'm going to sit here quietly and let you do just as you please?"

"Very quietly, as you say."

"Well, you've got another think coming!"

And he rears up and blocks the doorway.

Barabbas scratches himself copiously and queries everyone with his eyes. Come on now! Aren't times bad enough without blocking each other's road? He's still got half a bottle of scotch left . . . a little shot all round and. . . .

"You're going to let me do as I please because it's your only chance to make it home without being arrested by customs. And prisoners who break custody get their sentences doubled."

Black Willy blinks but quickly recovers.

"If I go to prison it'll be for murder, because first I'll see you hang from one of those barn rafters in your nun's habit, you little witch!"

Sister Céleste, who has already begun to get dressed, stops flat just as she is about to take the veil and decides it's time to put this scoundrel in his place. She grabs the pitchfork Barabbas has happened to pick up and threatens to pass the trident through Black Willy's stomach. But Crache-à-Pic intervenes before anybody gets hurt.

"Okay, Black Willy, in that case it's everyone for himself. Are you going to cross first, or will you follow us?"

Black Willy doesn't know where she's leading him, but he knows he mustn't follow.

"I won't be crossing before *or* after you, because you're not crossing at all."

"I'm not crossing?"

"Never!"

"Well, well!"

"Well what?"

"Nothing, I was just thinking of Dieudonné."

"Ah! You think Dieudonné will miss you?"

"No, not miss me, but. . . ."

Black Willy waits for it.

"But what?"

Crache-à-Pic takes her time; time calms the bootlegger down despite himself, and works in her favour.

"Oh, nothing," she says, as mysterious as can be.

"Anyway," he says, "you're wasting your time, because I'll never let you go."

But she knows she hasn't been wasting it, and he will let her go. So she moves to the offensive.

"Barabbas, old chum . . . say, who ever gave you a nickname like that, anyway?"

"It's not a nickname. It's a real name out of the Bible."

"Okay, Barabbas. I want you to go round the convent to the front door and ring the bell three times. The porter will stick her nose through the grille and say three words in Latin. Answer whatever you like, she won't understand anyway. Then tell her to go and tell the Mother Superior that two of her fellow sisters . . . make sure you say fellow-sisters. . . ."

"Hey, hey!" Black Willy starts up, jerking himself out of his astonishment. "Don't you budge an inch, Barabbas!"

Now it's Crache-à-Pic who seems to be astonished.

"Listen, Black Willy, I'm willing to admit you've got us hooked good and proper, me and Céleste, but that doesn't mean everyone's got to go down on their knees to you. Barabbas here, he's never done you any harm — why, he even offered you a drink, if I'm not mistaken. So how about showing a little more respect, eh?"

Black Willy can't get over this bald-faced show of naked nerve. At the very instant he has her in his power and could squash her on the wall, she snaps her fingers at him and laughs in his face. Well, she won't get away with it this time. And he charges.

But his move is checked by an engine-noise which makes him turn his head towards the Ford, which Ti-Louis the Whistler is cranking up. Ti-Louis caught on to his chief's strategy from the very first words of this verbal battle, and has now entered the game. Crache-à-Pic is quite capable of playing three chess matches at once. Not so Black Willy; he hasn't been trained for judo and debate at the same time. And the Whistler has slipped between his legs.

"Come on now, make up your mind," says Crache-à-Pic. "You little vixen!"

"Well now, the little vixen's going to surprise you, my old wildcat! I'm going to make you remember till you're old and grey, if you live that long, that Crache-à-Pic never forgets a favour, no more than a blow below the belt. Dieudonné wasn't afraid to bring his airplane out of hiding last fall, to join the others looking for my brother Tobie by flying over the trees. That was asking a lot, to get Dieudonné to air his secret. Well, today I'm squaring with him. I'm ready to get you across the line without a single customs man even thinking of picking you up."

This speech was so long and so well made that Black Willy, expert in the cutting unfinished phrase, stood hypnotized like a rattlesnake. At which point Crache-à-Pic made a sign to Céleste to pass her the coif.

And there on the barn floor, under the eyes of a bootlegger and a vagabond, the two Sisters dressed up in their habits again to the sound of a harmonica playing in a minor key:

You take my crown
It is your own
In Heaven, I know,
You'll give it back to me.

To console himself for the departure of his friends, Barabbas sat stroking his new coat, his shirt, and his dark blue pinstripe pants, which had belonged to Black Willy but which Crache-à-Pic had made him exchange for the tramp's rags.

"If you don't want to be recognized, do as I say," she ordered, smearing the smuggler's face with dried cow-dung. "And remember to keep your trap shut. From now on you're a deaf-mute that two Sisters of Charity are taking back to an old folks' home."

They had decided to go back by the north, crossing the border at Madawaska, for Black Willy had confessed to Crache-à-Pic that in the south they were on the lookout for a pair of "goddam little nuns". When it was a question of getting home safely, Black Willy preferred to put all the odds on his side and get back in one piece. He'd have the rest of his life to get back at that damned lousy little slut of a bitch!

They drove day and night, Black Willy and Ti-Louis the Whistler taking turns at the wheel while the two nuns, stowed in the rumble seat, veils streaming in the wind, sang obscene songs to hymn tunes:

The bumptious parish priest
Went out to hunt one day,
With gun and dog and all
He started on his way.
He came across a toad
And hoisted up his gun,
Took aim and fired
And O my God!
He shot him in . . .
The bum . . . ptious parish priest. . . .

One morning when Sister Holy Spittle of the Child Jesus and Sister Celestial Stars were exchanging samples of Latin, in the style of:

    Et in coelo et in terra

    If you're smelly-o, change your underweara . . .

a sudden shower burst over their heads. Before they had time to close the rumble-seat and jump into the back of the car, they were blinded simultaneously: their coifs, stiffened with potato starch, had flopped over their eyes.

So the two "goddam little nuns" were rigged out in habits that no congregation of pontifical or diocesan authority would ever have recognized when they replied to the indiscreet questions of Canadian Customs.

"Born . . . ?"

"Yes."

"Citizens . . . ?"

"Of the country."

"Residence . . . ?"

"Convent of the Immaculate Conception."

"How long you been away?"

"The time it takes to get there and back."

"Reason for the trip?"

"Good reason."

"Aim of your journey?"

"Right on target."

"Okay, Céleste. . . . The first aim was to drop off a blind man, the second was to pick up a deaf-mute. There he is . . . right there."

And lifting a corner of her wilting veil, Crache-à-Pic nods towards Black Willy, sitting there deaf as a piano-tuner.

"His name?"

"Ildefonse Laporte, Short-Ass Laporte to his friends."

Black Willy clenches his fists and begins to mutter, but at that very moment Ti-Louis stomps on his little toe projecting from a hole in Barabbas's old shoe, and Black Willy gives up with a sigh.

"All Canadian subjects?"

"Subject to all kinds of. . . . "

But Crache-à-Pic cuts Céleste short with a suave:

"Yes indeed, my son, thanks be to God. We will pray for you."

And she presses a coin into the hand of the customs officer who, surprised and pleased by the answers to his interrogation, salutes the company and waves them on down the road to the convent.

When Crache-à-Pic could finally stop laughing and catch her breath, the religious vehicle had already left Madawaska County and was rolling along a sideroad through the forest. Black Willy must have thought briefly of throwing all this fine company overboard and continuing on alone. But he didn't feel strong enough to fight, for he hadn't eaten in two days; and besides, he wouldn't have known what to say back at Sainte-Marie-des-Côtes, where there would surely be a crowd waiting for Crache-à-Pic and her crew on the outskirts of the village.

He was wrong by one sideroad; they were waiting at the end of Lovers' Lane.

It was there that Black Willy decided he'd had enough of travelling, jumped from the car, and took to the woods without so much as a thank you. Crache-à-Pic waved after him shouting,

"Go tell Dieudonné we're quits now and I don't owe him a thing."

And she let Ti-Louis make his way between the two lines of inquisitive poachers-loafers-pipe-smokers-hangers-on-of-the-forge, who had been advised by their counterparts in Village-des-Trois-Maisons that Crache-à-Pic was on her way home safe and sound from her seal-hunt.

Old Clovis chuckled:

"Never saw anyone around here hunt seal after the ice was out. But you've got to admit that this year we've seen plenty of marvels we never saw before."

And taking two Kings by the arms, he invited the third to follow them to Cap-Lumière.

Crache-à-Pic went straight to the apple tree where Tobie spent all his time and energy nowadays training his bear. He had already taught him to sit up, to stand on his hind feet, to unwind his chain from around the trunk of the tree, to growl softly, to walk on velvet paws, and to lick the hand of his master who fed him on acorns, beechnuts, apples, and wild berries.

"Taking good care of him, Tobie?"

And Tobie was delighted to show off his friend and protégé.

Next Crache-à-Pic went over to Adalbert . . . no, Dagobert . . . and asked if the bear had taken good care of Tobie. And the Twin reassured her. From now on Crache-à-Pic would have a freer rein: Cap-Lumière was well guarded.

"No Crache-à-Pic has ever had to call on a constable for help yet, never. I don't want it said that one day I had to ask handsome Martial to come over to defend the last of the line."

The Twin opened his mouth wide enough to let out a whole sentence.

"Constable Martial won't be coming over to Cap-Lumière ever again, bear or no bear."

. . . ?

"Constable Martial has left the country."

Since earliest childhood Crache-à-Pic had always wanted to know everything, but hated having to ask questions to find out. She usually tried to reach her goal by moving perpendicularly. "When you go to heaven," her mother said, "you'll take the shortest path up." And Céleste had added, "Yes, probably a sideroad."

She looked Dagobert straight in the eye and waited. It was Adalbert who replied.

"Martial was recalled because of the Hallowe'en ghosts, but mainly on account of that Santa Claus," he said.

But the crowd that had greeted them at the outskirts of the village and had come running along behind their car was already pouring into the Crache-à-Pics' yard. This seal-hunt on the bay completely free of ice was too spectacular and risky an adventure to let the first words fall on vulgar ears, and Old Clovis wanted to be the first to hear.

But this time the old storyteller was disappointed. Though Crache-à-Pic treated him and his chums to a glass of the best whisky and put a good face on it, Clovis, true connoisseur that he was, could tell her heart wasn't in it. Virtuoso though she might be, today she didn't even bother to accompany her story with her left hand. Clovis tried to help her, suggesting images, leading her into allegory. . . . Come on, Crache-à-Pic, your audience is familiar. You could tell the whole thing without ever naming the border, the States, the habit (carefully sent back via Jimmy-the-Flea to be hung on its nail on the convent back porch). She could relive her whole glorious adventure on the open sea between seals and hunters, and every one of her avid listeners would know exactly what name to apply to the seals in question.

"You must have been pretty hot under the collar now and then," urges Balthazar.

But she won't take the bait; she lets Céleste reply. Behind her godmother's babble she can hear shreds of another conversation that the Twins are teasing out of a bent old man leaning on the gatepost.

. . . Martial had to go because of the stolen cars the flabby-ass didn't pick up in time, and because he stupidly let them get dumped into the bay. A good fellow, that Martial was, a local boy who knew everybody, but in times like these you can't afford to go around playing hide-and-seek or hoist-the-sail.

"There's even some say things aren't going too good in the Old Countries, and when things start to spoil over there. . . . Even hear tell the States could be going to abolish their Prohibition. Which means the fellows who pull the strings up in Ottawa must have figured it might be a good idea to shorten them up a trifle. On account of because those bootleggers, when they see their last hour drawing nigh, will sure as shooting cast off all the lines and fly all the canvas they can. Which is why Martial got sent somewhere else and they got someone new for Sainte-Marie-des-Côtes, someone who . . . well, someone who's something more of a man."

At that instant Crache-à-Pic lifts her head. She hasn't seen or heard anyone, but she lifts her head towards the horizon just the same. And abandoning her guests — grown more and more numerous with the addition of women and children — to Céleste's bubbling, burgeoning account of their crazy adventures, she slips away and heads straight for the dock.

It is dusk, that clear dusk of the longest days of the year. She is alone. As she always does at times like this, she talks to her dear dead ones. To her father and grandfather, an old habit she has had since childhood; to her brothers, too, whom she's never seen again; and for the past year, just a year to the day now, to her mother. Death has never frightened Crache-à-Pic, no more than the unknown, the mysterious, the foreign. She doesn't think about it, doesn't question it, though sometimes she feels it brush against her at evening and whisper words in her ear. But these words always have the same resonance, always evoke the same images in her head — images of the sea, of a tree, of a field of wheat, of the wind, images of life. And Crache-à-Pic laughs at death, for it inspires her with a love of life.

. . . Once again the sun has cast its ladder of blood across the sea. Tomorrow will be hot. They'll take the *Sea-Cow* out early. . . . Someone is moving on the deck . . . has it come to that now, someone searching her schooner by night? No, he's standing up on the fo'c's'le, standing straight, facing the sea. It's someone come to sniff the air, to take in the evening. And from the deck of the *Sea-Cow* the view is so much broader . . . fresher. . . .

She doesn't move. He's seen her. And he's coming towards her. She knows it's him, the new constable. Well, well! He'll be quite a mouthful! Martial was nothing but cat mush. But this one . . . the old gaffer said he'd be more of a man . . . it's true. So much the better. It'll make the game more fun.

He stops ten paces from her. She has time to pick out his features. Does he look like an Indian or a Viking? Neither. An older race. He must go back to. . . .

He's spoken to her. She's heard his voice. And she is about to reply. A single phrase comes to her mind: "Now it's the two of us!" But she says nothing. For at the same instant she sees, standing on the sand on the far side of the creek, the silhouette of big Dieudonné. And the phrase that finally crosses her lips makes the new constable cock his eye:

"Now it's the three of us!"

CHAPTER FOUR

"IT WAS ALL GOD'S FAULT," CLOVIS THE STORYTELLER TOLD my father one day when he was almost one hundred. "You see, the weather was just too good that summer."

Too good! Oh yes, my father knew what that meant. So good the very earth was sweating brine. And you know how thirsty salt makes you, what a hole it digs in your stomach. The country had never felt such a need to shovel it in as they did in the summer of '31. Especially after that long winter. But during the fishing season nobody on the coast has to go around rubbing his belly, with his tongue hanging out.

"In July and August, Joe Beef puts away his butcher hooks, takes down his nets, and calls himself Joe Fish."

And even the poor and the needy get to eat fresh cod, lobster, and salmon-trout. And then they get thirsty.

A good summer all right, if an odd one!

Good, that is, for everyone except Dieudonné. According to Zéphirine the poor man had to recondition his stomach with big glasses of Epsom salts and doses of milk of magnesia. A whole truckload of whisky seized at the American border, just fancy that! Plus a ruse revealed, his honour smirched, and a man in prison. Never mind the man—Dieudonné had replaced him almost at once. Unemployment hit one out of every two heads of family in those days, and every morning the bootlegger saw ragged men coming down from the back country or sprouting up from points and dunes to line up at his barn door looking for work. He replaced the Colossus with two poachers, brothers from Grand-Digue who'd had a run in with the fisheries officers in forbidden waters the night before.

"I'll take the two of you for the price of one," Dieudonné offered.

And the Grand-Digue brothers nodded yes, their eyes on the horizon.

But it wasn't so easy to replace the truck. Because if there was one thing that wasn't unemployed in those days. . . . Trucks, boats, wagons, even the little airplanes that buzzed and swooped, day or night, between the horns of the cattle standing in the fields . . . anything that flew, floated, or rolled along the sideroads or portages was very much in demand on the coast in the thirties.

Dieudonné raged and swore vengeance.

He raged against life, which had thrown that lousy slut of a wench, Crache-à-Pic, into his path a year ago. What business was it of hers anyway? Wasn't she happy enough in the hold of her cargo-ship, polishing up the officers' brass buttons? Couldn't she have stayed there, lost in the southern seas? She would have to come back, wouldn't she, and break into the game on his own private preserve, and draw into her wake at Cap-Lumière that whole crowd of empty-bellied, downtrodden bums who used to hang around the bootleggers' barns.

. . . It was a nasty swing of the weathercock for Dieudonné, said Clovis, to see it lurch around to the Crache-à-Pics' broken-down dock, sending all the loafers, dreamers, and tipplers of the country over there to spend every morning trading tall tales and remaking the world in the shadow of the *Sea-Cow.*

And with an air of distraction Crache-à-Pic let the golden stream of rum and scotch whisky flow into those open beaks, almost as if by accident.

"Christ Almighty!" complained the king of the Three Kings, "we managed to sniff out all Black Willy's secrets. How come we can't find Crache-à-Pic's hideaway?"

Because Crache-à-Pic knew how to keep her mouth shut. So well that even Old Clovis was often led to wonder by what subterfuge — he called it "trick of the devil" — she'd succeeded in getting her hands on the old retreat house's reserve.

"And to begin with, how did she crack the secret? How did Crache-à-Pic dig out that particular hiding-place?"

The old boy was forgetting that he'd known it himself at the time of the ghosts' visit. And that he hadn't been able to resist the itch to hint it away. Like all storytellers of his ilk, Old Clovis specialized in feints, provocations, and I-know-what-I-know-but-I-won't-tell poses. He would have found it beneath his dignity to reveal everything from A to Z. But Crache-à-Pic, who had conch-shell ears and palpitating nostrils and didn't keep her eyes in her pockets, as my father used to say, was clever at turning old delvers of family relations into informers — without the relations being any the wiser.

So it was that during that famous summer of '31, so hot the seagulls drooped and the fields of oats ripened as gold as wheat, Crache-à-Pic won over the country.

And everybody — except Marie-Pet, the doctor's family, the presbytery and the convent, and a few other families who, without going so far as to call them respectable, one might have said were attached to certain traditions — everybody got involved in the grand game of petty contraband. No one would have thought of going so far in the days of Constable Martial . . . poor man, it wasn't his fault he came from Pré-d'en-Haut. . . . In those days crafty characters the likes of the Three Kings or Zéphirine or Alisca or Xavier-the-Hunchback would never have knocked themselves out to set traps for a poor devil who was generally walking backwards with both feet in the same boot. But with the arrival of a new representative of the law. . . .

"Quicksilver was his name, or nickname. And I'll tell you why. First off, on account of because everyone on the coast has a nickname, whether it's official or not. And second because this particular fellow, even if he was a foreigner come from another land, seemed so much like people around here that it would have been an insult to call him by his right name. But don't look at me, it wasn't me who nicknamed him. Nor Melchior either, for once. Seems it was Old Ozite."

Clovis didn't have to dig very deep into his grey matter to guess that, for Old Ozite was responsible for half the nicknames circulating in the country. The Three Kings themselves, to begin with. But for Quicksilver she'd had to look a bit further.

"When he first landed at the dock," she's supposed to have said, "the new officer had wings on his heels."

No kidding!

And century-old Clovis, reporting the words of the hundred-plus Ozite more than thirty years later, chuckled at such senility.

He came from abroad, this new constable, yet it was as if he came from around here. Originally from Saint-Pierre and Miquelon, he had the same ancestors as the Martins from this coast, Clovis decided, delving the constable's family tree. But that would be going all the way back to the Deportation. Supposedly. Which didn't prevent him from speaking the same language as his cousins, or almost.

"He has just a wee bit of an accent," Clovis went on. "He talks thick like folks from Cocagne. But he speaks clear."

"With a handsome mug like that, anybody'd speak clear."

"And not only his mug. Did you see his eyes?"

"Hard to make out under those big bushy eyebrows dangling down from his forehead."

"A forehead as broad as the cheeks of your bum side by side, Gaspard. If I was one of your bulls, I'd try not to cross horns with him."

"If I was a bootlegger, I wouldn't leave my barn door open this winter."

"I'd leave nothing at all open, no matter who I was."

And all the pipe-smokers spat to one side in unison, without looking at anyone in particular.

Crache-à-Pic paid no attention to this gossip from forge and fish-shed, and didn't bat an eye under the stream of spit-borne tattle. Not an eyelash. Barely twitched her nose.

So Old Clovis thought it best to add for good measure,

"There's some say Martin, others Mathieu. So it's got to be either Martin Mathieu, or else Mathieu Martin. Whichever, it's still a name from the coast. That's clear."

It was clear. And firm. And the coast was to learn in the month that followed that the new constable had no intention of fooling around with apprentice bootleggers.

"Just remember that fine fellow Tilmon-à-Tilmon, wild young scatterbrain that he was, singing *Honneur à la patri-i-e!*

through the bars of the jail window on the Feast of the Assumption!"

His mother was the only one in the procession of the faithful going up to the church who didn't laugh. A son in prison is no laughing matter! During the lobster-fishing season, too! And all the fault of those bandits of bootleggers. Célestine had to cross three fields and four snake fences to go and console old mother Tilmon, and explain to her that if her son was in prison it was because he'd been luckier than the others, that was all.

. . . Luckier?

. . . Luckier, I say.

And Célestine set out to relate the chain of events to the tearful mother, and for the benefit of Clovis, too; he happened to be there listening, and told the story to my father thirty years later, in Célestine's own words. . . .

. . . Luckier, I say, because it was none other than Tilmon who happened by chance on the hidden store of booze in the dune. You can see how it was: this young lad going off duck-hunting, going after the small black duck, so he was, quite legal, out there on the dune that's everybody's property, on a day that was neither a holiday nor one of your stinking hot dog-days — there he was then, minding his own business and not hurting a fly. Well, it so happens that sitting down on the dune to roll a cigarette — a young fellow twenty-five and making good money has a right to smoke outside of Lent and Advent, doesn't he? — well, dropping down on the sand, as I say, he sees one of his heels sinking in more than it should. That strikes him. It's a curious thing when one of your feet digs itself into a sand dune all on its own, while the other stays on top as quiet as you please. So this Tilmon, he begins to wonder if he isn't sitting in the middle of some quicksand. . . . Come on now, Tilmon! Quicksand on a sand dune? What next! If that was possible we'd have heard of it long ago. . . . When he reached that point in his reasoning he saw that he couldn't see his ankle any more, or his shank, and that his knee would soon be underground, and that it was high time to yank himself up out of this mess if he wasn't going to find himself buried alive and kicking. But when he went to get up, darned if his leg didn't sink in up to . . . up to here — and Célestine showed where with her hand. . . .

"And in the time it takes to say an Act of Contrition, that scatterbrain Tilmon began to look like a pirate who'd lost his wooden leg."

Hearing the beginning of a laugh whistling on the lips of old Mother Tilmon, Célestine plunged on.

. . . He never did finish that prayer, the lucky devil, because his toes had just met up with something under the dune that seemed to resemble a chest . . . or a crate . . . or a gallon tin! If that Tilmon had been better educated, he'd have struck up a tea *Deum* right then and there, instead of *O My Darling Clementine* — for he'd just uncovered one of the bootleggers' biggest and richest stores, by pure good luck and pure chance.

Old Clovis had to comment on this; it was only fair.

"To my way of thinking there was no more good luck in that than there's bad luck in the death of a soldier. Sooner or later a fighting man comes face to face with death, for the very good reason that on the battlefield death is hiding everywhere . . . it's just a question of time. And likewise, the coast in those days was a regular rum-running no-man's-land with jugs and cans and barrels hidden all over the place.

Sooner or later even a scatterbrain was bound to stumble across something. But they called him lucky."

" . . . Except that Tilmon's luck," Célestine continued, "turned against him the day someone else who was even luckier discovered his hidden treasure."

A newcomer to the trade, Scatterbrain Tilmon hadn't taken enough precautions, and hadn't observed Crache-à-Pic's golden rule. He talked. Without ever saying anything in particular, he revealed everything: the place, the number of cans, the trademark stamped on the tin . . . not Hand Brand by any chance? I'll never believe it! . . . and just how much he counted to make from this heaven-sent good fortune. That was his first mistake. . . . How much he hoped to make? So Scatterbrain was planning to take up bootlegging himself instead of simply and generously sharing his find with his skirt-chasing, fun-loving buddies?

And his buddies began following him around, watching him, studying his smallest gestures; in short, they declared war on him. And the poor hunted creature, not knowing which way to turn, finally stepped right into the trap.

A trap set by Edmond-à-Arcade but based on an idea, so it seems, from Ti-Louis the Whistler. According to Clovis. Ti-Louis didn't belong to any gang, which allowed him to hand out his ideas freely to whoever wanted them, first come first served, without haggling over the profits. An artist, that's what he was. So quite by chance he had sown this idea in Edmond's ear. Our fine friend Edmond was twice as old as the Whistler, and consequently was twice as thirsty and had half as many scruples.

One day, wide-eyed and out of breath, he rushed into Tilmon's place where Tilmon sat quietly cleaning his gun.

"Get up off your ass!" he said. "You've got half an hour to save all your stuff!"

"What are you talking about?" said Tilmon, springing up.

"I'm telling you, there's no time to lose if you want to save what you're hiding."

'Me? . . . I'm not hiding anything."

"Oh well, in that case you've got nothing to lose, so you can sit down again. All you've got to do is tell Quicksilver to his face that you're not hiding anything."

The name Quicksilver put springs in Scatterbrain Tilmon's legs, and he grabbed his friend by the shoulders.

"Goddam it to hell, Edmond! You've got to help me!"

"Let's hide it in the woods."

"No, it's too risky. I hear Quicksilver knows the woods as well as any partridge hunter. We'll have to stick to the coast."

"The coast? Are you crazy? The Three Kings are always hanging around there now the fishing season's started."

True enough, thought Tilmon the fisherman; the only ones to stay on shore during the fishing season, just to mock the others, were the poachers who were out at sea all the rest of the year.

Edmond had a better idea.

"How about using the little chapel the nuns have at the end of the Calvary . . . ?"

So the cans of Hand Brand made their way from cross to cross up the Calvary, to the little chapel the sisters never used except for feasts of the Blessed Virgin.

"And we'll have it all drunk up before August fifteenth," laughed Edmond, which made Scatterbrain Tilmon stop dead at the station of Pilate washing his hands and feel a serpent's bite where his heart should have been.

But he checked himself.

"When the danger's past I'll pay you for your trouble,

Edmond-à-Arcade. Say three gallons . . . will that make you happy?"

Edmond's dreams of happiness grew with each station of the cross as he carried the treasure up the Calvary. By the time he reached the chapel. . . . But all he said was a sublimely indifferent "Pshaw!", which Tilmon swallowed down like rattlesnake poison.

. . . He coughed it up a couple of days later, though — along with his last supper — in the chapel, at the foot of Saint Joseph leaning on his flowering stick and chuckling to himself under his plaster suit. But the saint was wrong to laugh, for in his rage Tilmon broke his arm clean off, and the flowering stick came crashing down on the marble altar.

"The little son of a bitch!" Scatterbrain finally managed to choke out, crossing himself before the Virgin. "I'll make him pay for this."

He paid.

For two days was all the time Edmond-à-Arcade needed to commit the same errors as Tilmon. Without admitting anything openly, he treated his thirsty buddies to the smile of a Christopher Columbus who knows China's not China but America, but knows he's the only one who knows. Well! Just great! If you think that Champdoré, Bois-Joli, and Village-des-Trois-Maisons were going to put up with that, think again. So they began to follow him around.

When Scatterbrain Tilmon finally caught up with him, the robber himself had just been robbed, so their quarrel ended in a single curse issued against all the rest of the country.

And so it went. From Tilmon to Edmond to Pierre to Jean to Jacques, the prize of the dune slipped from hand to hand and from hideout to hideout . . . until the day one of the boys from Sainte-Marie-des-Côtes opened his eyes, rubbed his thighs, and proposed a deal. Since it was evident that the territory was too big for one, and too small to divide up. . . . Come on, Foxtail, what are you driving at?

"I've got a terrible thirst," he replied.

So, without another "if" or "but" or "on account of because", everyone agreed to the proposition.

. . . You couldn't ask Célestine to go on and tell how the tipplers finished up in the cemetery, or who the heathen was who had the idea of hiding what was left in a grave . . . two or three graves it would take, but then the cemetery was full of them, there wasn't much else in a cemetery . . . graves, and their crosses over them . . . just a few good shovelfuls and then. . . . Hey! Not that one, Foxtail! You're digging up your father-in-law. Find one old enough so the ghost doesn't come up shouting out his name and showing his face . . . preferably an Irishman, out of respect for the holy Catholic apostolic French religion . . . and don't anybody forget that it's me, Tilmon, who found it in the dune in the first place, and that . . . aaaaah . . . !

Scatterbrain Tilmon's cry pushed Bois-Joli into Champdoré into Village-des-Trois-Maisons who pushed Sainte-Marie-des-Côtes into the nearest open grave. And it was there, in the tomb of the defunct Crooked O'Leary, that a good portion of our nocturnal gravediggers were caught red-handed, arrested, and relieved of fifty-six gallons of almost pure alcohol.

Quicksilver charged all seven of them, standing there as shame-faced as the seven deadly sins. One year after the carnival of Lovers' Lane, the new constable was here to demonstrate to Black Willy and Dieudonné that an apparition doesn't need a sheet and a set of bones to pass for a ghost.

"For nothing is more like death than the fear of death," proclaimed Old Clovis, quoting scripture.

But Quicksilver's real catch that night was not the seven scatterbrains who'd taken him for the ghost of old O'Leary, and were only guilty of drinking the hooch. It was the notice he served the whole country that Martial was likely to have a prolonged vacation, and that henceforth the constable was the man from Saint-Pierre and Miquelon.

In the light of strange phosphorous glimmerings he rapped out,

"And who does the reserve belong to at the time of this interrogation?"

The reply was not long coming, and echoed in chorus,

"To Scatterbrain Tilmon of Sainte-Marie-des-Côtes."

. . . So that's how Tilmon-à-Tilmon, known as Scatterbrain, ended up in the county jail and received his share of liquid cheer every night from the hands of his contrite companions. And that's how Célestine convinced the tearful mother that her son had been lucky.

That old dog Clovis had learnt at the same time — excuse me, an hour before all the rest of the coast — about the discovery on the dune, and had followed the odyssey of the gallon cans from the crosses on the Calvary to the little chapel to the dock to the cemetery with a good head start; he now concluded that Martial's day was definitely done. "From here on in . . . ," he said. . . .

And the whole forge knew exactly what he meant.

Yet nobody had a bad word for Martial. He was a great guy. As good as fresh-baked bread. As honest in the practice of his trade as the day is long. He was in the habit of paying little courtesy calls, as casual as you please, to the most suspicious homes in the village at about the same time every month, calls of the "just happened to be passing by and bring you greetings from the family" kind. Since nobody so honoured had any relations in the police force, they never did get out the dandelion wine or bathtub beer to welcome such a shameless visitor. And certainly never a jug of Hand Brand — not bloody likely.

Sometimes, however, the visit would come a day off schedule, by inadvertence or accident . . . mustn't blame Martial . . . and one or another of these petty hooch-makers would be caught with his pants down around his ankles.

Clovis remembers one of these courtesy calls when Tom-à-Ozite was nearly found with his hand in the still, where he was boiling off a concoction of his own made with a base of wild wheat. The suspicious aroma had already invaded the summer kitchen, the winter kitchen, the store-room, and the plastered bedroom, and was just about to reach the nostrils of the just-passing-by-and-bring-you-greetings constable when old centenarian Ozite threw him off the scent with a yell that brought her distraught daughter-in-law running to the side of her rocking-chair. The daughter-in-law found a bottle of rubbing alcohol thrust at her.

"Rub me backbone," the old girl mumbled, with a long groan that drew a sigh of compassion even from the law.

And the most stubbornly healthy centenarian in the country sat like a lamb to have her back and thighs rubbed down under the prudish nose of a constable who couldn't distinguish the smell of rubbing alcohol from homemade whisky. Wishing Madame Ozite a quick recovery, he stammered out his just-passing-by — and the whole family thanked him for bringing news of the family.

But with the landing of Quicksilver at Sainte-Marie-des-Côtes the days of Martial, repeated Clovis, were numbered. Before he'd even raised his little finger Quicksilver had let the coast know that from now on, not to say henceforward, the battle was on between the two sides — three, if you counted the neutrals. The events at the cemetery did nothing more than confirm Clovis's presentiment.

And Crache-à-Pic's presentiment more than anyone's.

Since her spring in the States Crache-à-Pic could be seen every day at the wheel of her four-pedal Ford, crossing Sainte-Marie-des-Côtes from north to south, east to west, and sometimes even west to north, cutting corners off the King's Highway and giving Marie-Pet a stiff neck.

"That little good-for-nothing will end her days at the foot of the cliff, you mark my words!"

But the day the rumble-seat was seen overflowing with gleeful children like buds on a rosebush, and Marie-Pet had time to make out that one of them was a Caissie, the grandmother hoisted up her skirts and dashed after them in a swirl of dust.

"Stop them! Stop them!"

And Clovis roared with laughter.

Crache-à-Pic was still full of inventions. What officer of the law could mistrust a fine girl who'd generously drive a bunch of inoffensive underprivileged kids up and down the hills of Village-des-Trois-Maisons in her car? And what lout would go around inspecting a rumble-seat stuffed with brats singing *Yippee-kye-o-kye-yay*?

But while chuckling to himself, Clovis squinted in the direction of the Three Kings, who were going around the village killing themselves laughing. The wizened old gaffer reminded Sainte-Marie-des-Côtes, "He who laughs on a Friday ends up bawling by Sunday."

To which the young fry replied, "Today's Thursday, so anything goes!" and roared all the louder. Even right under Quicksilver's nose, when he was peering at the horizon over by Cap-Lumière one evening.

"This Crache-à-Pic . . . ," he said.

And everyone drew breath right down to the bottom of their lungs.

"Crache-à-Pic? Why, what can I say? She's the kind of girl would make your little dog's tail wag, that's for sure."

Quicksilver smiled. "Meanwhile she's stirring up quite a bit of dust over the marsh hay and the wheat-fields," he said.

But the young fry were all unconditionally on Crache-à-Pic's side; they'd never whisper a word of her adventures to a man of the law, no, not a word, unless it was:

"All I can say is, the day of her wedding God knows who'll be leading who up the aisle."

There were lots of laughs left for the constable. One day, like a real contrabandist doing things up in style, Crache-à-Pic invented a code. You can imagine the savoury messages you could put together with *bumptious, bumpkin, bum-boat, bumble-bee, bumper, bum-boy, stumblebum,* and *bumf.*

"Go find *bumpkin,* Tobie, and tell him to come around in the *bumble-bee.*"

But Tobie came back half an hour later with his arms dangling and his tongue hanging out. He'd looked on the dock, in the schooner, at Céleste's place, and he hadn't been able to find Jimmy-the-Flea anywhere.

"In that case get Ti-Louis the Whistler, and hurry. *Bumpkin* must be out digging clams."

Tobie opened his mouth but closed it again. He'd already forgotten what it was he wanted to say about Jimmy. So he went off looking for Ti-Louis.

"A guy who knows how to drive a *stumblebum* should be able to manage the *bumble-bee*," said Crache-à-Pic.

Ti-Louis understood and made his way to the barn, where he took out an old hunk of junk that had once been a truck. In her bum-code Crache-à-Pic explained to her men that they were to load this vehicle with the best *bumf* and drive north. Meanwhile she took a jug of rum and soaked the rumble-seat and the hood of the four-pedal Ford with it.

Céleste frowned.

"My father always used to say that luck never smiles on the wasteful."

Crache-à-Pic put her hands on her godmother's shoulders.

"And didn't he ever tell you not to judge by appearances?"

After many recommendations to Ti-Louis and the Twins about where to *bump* the *bumble-bee*, the *stumblebum*, and the *bum-boat*, she climbed into her little Ford and made the gravel fly. She drove back and forth in front of the Babineaus' store, the church, the bank, the Légers' place, the Collettes', the Allains', drawing more and more curious spectators out on their front porches to sniff the air—which was strangely piquant to the nostrils that morning. When Marie-Pet's nose finally began to twitch, Crache-à-Pic knew it was time to hit the highway and drive south.

Her plan worked. Soon Quicksilver took off after her at top speed, bouncing over the gravel and the ruts and smelling the rum two miles away. When he finally managed to catch up with her, he searched her, clenched his teeth, and gave her a ticket for speeding.

"Not bad," he said, trying to hide his admiration.

For he had just figured out that while chasing this wild hare across the fields, he had missed the big game taking the path through the woods.

Thus Crache-à-Pic continued to learn her trade every day, for she had a good head for it. But Quicksilver, who had as good a one — and well-proportioned, too — spent this time learning Crache-à-Pic. The struggle between them became more and more evenly matched, the gods smiling now on one, now on the other. To the point where Crache-à-Pic forgot her rival smugglers and concentrated all her energy on one adversary, Quicksilver.

"We'll see how far the rascal can go," she muttered one day, digging her nails into Céleste's forearm.

Céleste looked up at her. . . . A true Crache-à-Pic she was, with something of Aglaé in the corners of her lips, the depths of her eyes, and the length of her neck. A splendid, handsome creature of the Good Lord. If she took it into her head to fume, kick up her heels and catch fire . . . Jesus Christ . . . !

The smuggleress became bolder and bolder, more and more reckless, taunting the law right up to his own doorstep, playing with fire until she was almost sure to get her wings singed, then, in a last-moment pirouette, slipping away to hide in the shrouds of the *Sea-Cow*. And all just for laughs.

Quicksilver seemed to go along with the game . . . what am I saying, go along? . . . to take real pleasure in it. At any rate he kept firm hold of his end of the string, and chalked up more and more points.

There was the case of the dozens of jugs of homemade wine the Galoshes were delivering to l'Anse-aux-Outardes in the *bum-boat* (read: ambulance). Well! The ambulance was soon transformed into a hearse strewing dead bodies (read: earthenware crocks) all along the road. To the great joy of the locals who collected this manna almost between the constable's legs . . . but he finally did catch up with the *bum-boat*, and got the truth about its name.

This stroke of bad luck forced Crache-à-Pic to rewrite her glossary completely. To muddy the scent she abandoned scatology for liturgy.

"And it was Marie-Pet," chortled Clovis, "who was first to be exposed to the new code when one day she overheard a strange argument between the Twins and Jimmy-the-Flea in terms like *lace surplice, sponge in the holy-water font, curé's biretta, nun's veil, Saint Anthony's poor-box, Palm Sunday, little pot for burning incense,* and *Ecce Homo*.

To the great delight of Clovis and the whole country.

Then one fine day, in late autumn, Crache-à-Pic and her Galoshes disappeared for several days.

"Six," said Melchior.

"At least eight," put in Gaspard and Balthazar.

But Clovis knew, because he'd counted them, that it was seven, no more and no less.

Let's go for seven then!

For seven days the country was without a trace of Crache-à-Pic's gang.

"Let's hope nothing bad's happened to them," Célestine grumbled.

But Célestine was only pretending to fret, the quicker to get the true story from the heart-shaped lips of that nephew of hers, Ti-Louis, who had his orders.

"What orders?" snapped Célestine, angry with her cousin Céleste for having left without a word.

"Orders not to tell Dieudonné's men that the *Sea-Cow* has gone over to Cape Breton."

Ti-Louis pronounced this in a detached tone, as though he were a Royal Canadian Mounted Policeman entrusted with the safekeeping of the Great Seal of Canada . . . if the country had had a Great Seal in 1931. To make his exact meaning absolutely clear.

And Célestine, after winking and blinking and screwing up her eyes for a while, got the message.

The message was that she should relay the information *Sea-Cow to Cape Breton* by the usual channels, but in the reverse direction. This time, from Céleste via Ti-Louis to cousin Célestine, to her sister-in-law Zéphirine, Crache-à-Pic let Dieudonné know that she had put out to sea Cape Breton way. And Dieudonné, old fox that he was, and seasoned interpreter of half-truths and apocryphal messages, concluded that the hussy must already be off the coast of Saint-Pierre and Miquelon.

So he swung his organization into motion.

To begin with he got his telegraph working. In less than an hour his whole network was alerted. In less than a day his suspicions were confirmed: the *Sea-Cow* had just left Saint-Pierre, loaded down to the gunwales.

Dieudonné rubbed his hands. At last! Now you're going to pay me back my Bordeaux wines and Napoleon brandy, you slut! A hundred times over. You're going to spit up every last bottle, right out there on the high seas, and you'll spit up your damned soul too if you dare resist me . . . ! And he summoned his best men: the Damien boys, the poacher-brothers from Grand-Digue — good bootlegging material that — and Black Willy.

"Here's your chance," he said to his second-in-command.

And Black Willy understood that it was his last one.

But this time the wench couldn't escape him. During the summer Dieudonné had acquired the *Sail Alone*, a Newfoundland ship that enjoyed all the privileges of British registry. And Old Clovis, recalling those days for my father, brought up the facts together with a good quantity of bile.

"The offshore territorial limit was twelve miles for Canadian vessels and three for English. How's that for a royal law! That meant any old hulk flying the English flag could poop around under our officers' noses three miles off the coast, while a ship like the *Sea-Cow* came under the law's thumb when it was eleven and three-quarters and half of the last quarter off shore. That's the Commonwealth for you."

And Dieudonné was the first on the coast to profit from it. . . . Well, profit in a manner of speaking! Wait and see.

Meantime Black Willy's gang was jubilant and pushed ahead with their plans.

"What if the bitch tries to defend herself?" Black Willy hazarded, partly just to say something, and partly to probe his chief's most secret intentions.

But his chief made light of it.

. . . Crache-à-Pic? A woman, backed by a bunch of ragamuffins, standing against five tough thugs? You should be ashamed of yourself! . . . They were not to waste any more time. He would tell them in code, at the very last instant, the exact place the *Sea-Cow* would cross the twelve-mile limit. From there on they would have nine free miles to navigate right under the coastguard cutter's nose.

"And for the last three miles it'll be a picnic. A fleet of small boats will meet you at the line. I'll send out so many our fine-feathered friend Quicksilver won't know which one to follow first."

And they all spat in their hands and winked at the sky, as blue that morning as the Virgin's cloak.

Under that same sky Ti-Louis the Whistler came over to advise his friend Clovis that he had business in the north, up Caraquet way to be precise, had to look into a family matter.

Clovis knew the Whistler's family better than the Whistler himself, who knew no relations beyond Célestine, and understood that Ti-Louis's business must be liturgical in nature and that he was being asked in the name of friendship not to ask questions. So he blessed Ti-Louis with two fingers, like a bishop, and enjoined him to convey his greetings to the relations in question. Glad to make your acquaintance!

Whereupon Ti-Louis left in the *bumble-bee*, rebaptized the *sponge in the holy-water font*.

At Caraquet he went down to the dock and asked, on behalf of *Ecce Homo*, to speak to a certain Seraphim. He was led to the hold to a schooner where three men told him to sit down, offered him tea, and asked him to make himself at home.

"Shouldn't be long now," said one of the three, who answered best to the name of Seraphim but who, it turned out later, was called Shit-Shoveller. "Meanwhile make yourself comfortable."

Having lived a good hundred years in the short time he'd been in this country, Ti-Louis made himself comfortable and waited. In a day or two at the outside his contact would come, by night, right there at dockside. So he started looking out to sea, by sunlight and starlight, his heart swelling with gratitude and much else besides.

. . . It was Ti-Louis's first love since his dog died. And

how awkward it made him! That Christmas Eve it was doubtless thanks to her that he had finally decided not to die. . . .
No, that's not possible, Ti-Louis, you're off your rocker, you
didn't even know her then, that's the very night you met
her for the first time . . . what a woman! But don't go losing
your head, pal, she's not for you. She's at least old enough
to be your sister . . . if you'd had a sister . . . an older sister
who would have taken care of you . . . a sister, a mother,
everything you never knew. . . . Crache-à-Pic had replaced
them all with a single gesture, that Christmas Eve, when she
had gently removed the boots moulded to his feet like two
icicles.

"Women's boots!" she had exclaimed. "No wonder
his feet are coming through. Now who's the good Christian
dame makes it an act of charity to give a man a pair of
woman's boots?"

Célestine turned away. She'd have gladly given him her
own man's boots, but. . . . And Ti-Louis had said nothing.

Crache-à-Pic had unfrozen his ankles, then his heels,
then his toes, one after another, taking them in her hands,
and Ti-Louis's heart had grown so warm he'd stopped thinking about his feet. From that instant he had sworn never
again to try dying from the top of the bridge. Now he had
better things to do: he would give his life for Crache-à-Pic.

Crache-à-Pic never asked this sacrifice from any of her people, but at Saint-Pierre she asked even more of her Twins;
she separated them.

"Adalbert," she said, "I want you to take Jimmy aboard
the *Diable Vert* and go to Caraquet. Seraphim will be there
waiting for you with Ti-Louis. Dagobert, you stay with me
aboard the *Sea-Cow*."

For the first time in fifty years Adalbert and Dagobert would not be sleeping under the same roof or the same patch of sky or matching snores to the other's sighs.

Crache-à-Pic stood the first watch, sending Céleste and the Twin below. But Dagobert surfaced again a quarter of an hour later, as nervous as a mother hen counting and recounting her chicks.

"Come on now, Dagobert! The *Diable Vert* is friskier than any cutter in the north. The day after tomorrow they'll be landing at Caraquet, and I can trust Seraphim and his gang of *archangels*. At this very minute Ti-Louis is on his way, or is already there. He's probably playing his mouth-organ to keep the fish quiet."

The old fisherman shook his head as if to say he trusted the fish; the youngster would be better off trying to put the fisheries officers to sleep.

But most of all Dagobert would have liked to know, without asking too many questions, why Crache-à-Pic had gone to so much trouble to load a second boat when the schooner alone could easily have handled fifteen barrels of rum and a hundred and twenty cases of whisky. Not to mention the fact that Caraquet was the hell and gone away at the other side of the country; after running the risks by sea there'd be danger by land, for the road crossed half the province.

Crache-à-Pic listened in amazement to this man, who had never emitted so many sounds in his whole life; amputated from his brother, he showed twice as much energy, courage, and affection in defending Aglaé's daughter against her own ambition to remake the world in seven days.

"It's written that on the seventh day God rested, on account of because it was Sunday."

She burst out laughing to calm her faithful Twin, who was as agitated as an epileptic plagued by a premonition.

At dawn Céleste came grumbling up on deck . . . if you think it's any fun trying to sleep at sea in the month of November! If those guys from Saint-Pierre and Miquelon had put their minds to it they could have sold their barrels and jugs faster than that. And what kind of an idea is it to take the long way home when the sea belongs to everyone?

"We wound around so many islands last night that I came to this morning screwed up in my bunk like a pig's tail. If Jimmy and Adalbert did the same, our two ships will meet somewhere off Labrador."

Crache-à-Pic didn't listen. But her eyes said to Céleste that she'd made a mistake taking her out on the *Sea-Cow,* that next time. . . . How's that? And in the pitching and rolling of the boat Céleste pouted like a prince banished from his kingdom. The day the schooner went without her, someone would be sorry. They'd better not think they could leave Céleste behind!

The closer they came to Canadian territorial waters, the more the Twin felt ominous forebodings assailing him on every side. What if they made a slight swing to the south. . . .

"It wouldn't delay us very much to head for Cocagne and. . . ."

" . . . and fall right into Quicksilver's arms?" Crache-à-Pic countered, surprised at her slip . . . she had thought *hands* but she'd said *arms.*

Despite the sou'wester that covered her eyes and half her cheeks, Dagobert saw her blush. He turned away, and spotted the prow of a cutter cleaving the wave and bearing down on them.

"Coastguard! To port!"

Crache-à-Pic holds her breath, peers to port, then breathes again.

No, not the cutter. The *Sail Alone*. The *Sail Alone*, Dagobert, Dieudonné's latest find. Céleste screws up her mouth. Find! Find, my fanny! Dieudonné, my ass! Those rum-runners can. . . .

"Is Black Willy planning to cross the line in broad daylight?" Dagobert wonders. "Would he be sailing with an empty hold, then?"

Crache-à-Pic has a funny look on her face.

"If one of Dieudonné's ships crosses the twelve-mile limit with its head high, you can be sure it has plans in its noggin. Plans Quicksilver doesn't know about."

At that moment Dagobert realizes that Crache-à-Pic knows these plans, and that she's making ready to counter them with plans of her own, though he doesn't yet know how. In any case, he picks up a harpoon and stations himself in front of the women. On her mettle, Céleste tucks up her apron, jabs a hairpin through her bun, and prepares a string of epithets for any fine son of a whore baptized in sewer water who plans to show up. Crache-à-Pic slips into the front rank when Dagobert isn't looking, and is the first to receive the full force of the dragon's attack.

"Down sails! Everyone on deck! The first one who tries to escape will regret it."

. . . Not bad, Black Willy, not bad. Just like an order from an admiral of the British fleet. I don't know where the first one who tries to escape would escape to, since the *Sea-Cow* isn't fitted out with a back door giving onto the King's Highway, but. . . .

"Make yourself at home, captain. Step right in and take a neighbourly cup of tea."

But Black Willy has been brooding over his revenge

for a year and he's in no mood to play around, especially with women, and with this woman in particular. . . . Watch out, Black Willy, the wench has never played straight . . . don't get caught, Black Willy, take the bitch high and don't spare the whip.

The *Sea-Cow*'s sail shudders and lags as the prows shock together. Céleste's bun, too, shakes out and falls about her ears. Dagobert bends his knees, grasps his lance tighter, and blocks the way of the first of the Damien boys who has just jumped aboard. But at the same instant the other one comes over, followed by the poachers from Grand-Digue, and then Black Willy, who orders them to overpower the men on board.

The men on board? Aside from Dagobert, who's ready to fight to the finish, it's Céleste who is thrashing around like a devil in a holy-water font and yelling at the two Damien boys that the first son of a bitch who dares raise a hand against an honest Roman Catholic mother will never get the last rites on his deathbed or holy communion brought to his home on first Fridays when he's old and decrepit. And the Damien boys stand stymied by this flood, uncertain which religious threat applies to them.

At the same time the two poacher-brothers, who have often fraternized with the Twins at sea, are at the foot of the mainmast trying to figure out how to tackle and neutralize their fellow-fisherman without hurting him.

Meanwhile Black Willy, shouting and puffing, is demanding that the others be brought before him. . . . The others? What others?

. . . All right, Crache-à-Pic, since when does the *Sea-Cow* take off on an expedition like this with only half its crew?

. . . Oh, you mean them. . . .

"Where's the rest of the Twins, and where's that good-for-nothing Jimmy-the-Flea?"

And as he lifts his head to check the rigging and the sails . . . ouf! A knee from Céleste where he least expects it! She's ready to admit her son's a good-for-nothing, but reserves to herself the right to make it public.

Pow . . . ouch!

"That'll teach you, you good-for-nothing, to go around good-for-nothinging others."

Enraged and wild as a tiger, Black Willy grabs Céleste by the shoulders, spins her around, and sends her flying into a tangle of ropes where she lands, heels in the air, exposing to the view of the Damien boys all her endowments as a good Catholic matron. At least now they'll be spared having to lay hands on one of their mother's neighbours.

They turn towards Crache-à-Pic, who is leaning up against the mast, her sou'wester thrown back on her neck, watching the fight with dancing eyes. Dagobert is holding off the poachers all alone, and now he's threatening the Damiens with his fishing harpoon . . . watch it, Twin, no bloodshed, don't go too far, Dagobert, we're having fun.

But Céleste has managed to get to her feet again, and she's decidedly not having fun. From her matronly viewpoint, piracy is no joke, it's Dieudonné's dirty work, disgraceful, grrr! . . . ssss! . . . try if you dare! . . . and she throws an armful of rope between Black Willy's legs just as he's on the point of jumping on the Twin's back, which brings the traitor rolling down at Dagobert's feet. One of the Damien boys scratches his head as if remembering the picture in the big catechism of the Archangel Michael, spear in hand, setting his heel on a vanquished Lucifer.

What a great day it is!

But despite Céleste's cries — Scum! Riff-raff! You're an insult to your fathers and mothers! — Dagobert, attacked by five men, is finally winded. Whereupon Crache-à-Pic decides the battle has lasted long enough to show Dieudonné's men what stuff the *Sea-Cow* is made of.

"That's enough!" she shouts. "Stop!"

And all the men, used to recognizing a captain from the tone of voice, freeze.

"All right," she says, "let go the Twin and don't lay a hand on Céleste. And tell me what you're looking for."

Good Lord! What is it they're looking for? They can't remember. It's been a long time since the poachers had such a great fight. It's good for what ails you.

Then Black Willy comes to with a start.

"The others . . . Jimmy-the-Flea, Adalbert. . . ."

"Adalbert? There he is standing in front of you."

. . . ?

"What do you want with him?"

"I want Dagobert. Where is he?"

Dagobert steps forward.

The pirates' heads swivel from left to right . . . whatever happens, don't get taken in. . . . Black Willy loses his temper.

"I want the second Twin."

"He is the second," Céleste cuts in. "The first's in bed with hay fever."

Now Black Willy gets a mean look in his eye.

"Tie the Twin to the mast," he commands, "and go through this henhouse with a fine-tooth comb."

. . . Go ahead with your insults, Black Willy. You'll pay for them. You'll pay this very day. Don't worry, Céleste, and Dagobert, don't look so down in the mouth. Just let time run its course, and life, and fate — which is on our side today.

With round eyes Céleste and Dagobert watch the barrels of rum and cases of whisky come up out of the hold right under Crache-à-Pic's nose. She doesn't say a thing. Doesn't even lift a little finger to defend her cargo, and lets Black Willy sneer and spout proverbs about the sun breaking through after the rain and the seven fat cows following the seven lean ones.

"Just count yourselves lucky we aren't leaving anything on board," he spits in their faces, "or you might get picked up at the line by the coastguard."

He has a loud greasy laugh at that, while Crache-à-Pic laughs quietly to herself without twitching a lip.

"Maybe the coastguard isn't that far away," she says. "In your place I'd drink up those six barrels and thirty-two cases as quick as I could."

"Don't worry your head about us, Crache-à-Pic. We're running a Scottish Fisherman out of Newfoundland. Nobody has the right to touch us outside the three-mile limit, if you know the law."

She knows it, all right. Knows it a lot better than most lawmen that particular night. Better than Black Willy, anyway. And so he'll be sure to remember during those long winter nights behind bars, as the *Sail Alone* is about to move off she calls out,

"Don't forget, Black Willy, it's so many days in prison per case."

And her laughter explodes at the same time as the twin engines of the Scottish Fisherman.

Sainte-Marie-des-Côtes, Cocagne, Champdoré, and Village-des-Trois-Maisons would later scrap and squabble to see who could collect the best bits of this extraordinary story. In less than two years Crache-à-Pic, daughter of nobody, come from nowhere, had five times outsmarted the Master of the Gulf. And now, without any anaesthetic, she had yanked out his two front teeth.

It happened that very morning, out at sea. Dieudonné had been too busy planting traps for others to notice the noose tightening around his own neck, and the fool had sent his five best men straight into the jaws of the wolf.

Black Willy didn't understand it, couldn't get over it.

"We're within the law!" he shouted to the coastguard cutter that apprehended him. "We're within our rights! The *Sail Alone* is an English ship in international waters. You have no right to. . . ."

But Quicksilver paid no attention to these protests and ordered the ship seized.

"In whose name?"

"In the name of the law!"

"The law protects a British ship up to three miles from shore, sir."

"The law's been changed, sir. In future, Canadian territorial waters are twelve miles for everybody. Treaty of Westminster."

"The what? . . . Since when? . . . "

"Since midnight last night."

The bitch! Black Willy could just see Crache-à-Pic's face. According to Old Clovis, who swore to tell nothing but the truth, he even heard her laughter dancing over the crests of the waves.

And that's how come Black Willy, the two Damien boys, and the unlucky poachers from Grand-Digue who had just lost their boat to the fisheries officers, came to spend Christmas behind bars.

. . . So many days of prison per case, Black Willy! He swore he'd kill her.

This time Dieudonné had the same thought. That girl would be the death of him. Besides having to put up with the sick jokes that fumed up from every pipe and flapped on every clothesline on the coast, the Master of the Gulf had to decode congratulations telegraphed from Madawaska and Nova Scotia from belly-laughing friends. She'd asked for it, the slut! . . . And while he hadn't settled on any precise idea, he knew he would stop at nothing.

The welding of the Twins back together again in the little port of Cap-Lumière was the most touching scene Old Clovis registered in this whole chronicle of what he used to call the Grand Epoch.

The *Diable Vert* had landed before the *Sea-Cow*, as planned, which gave Ti-Louis time to bring his two friends back home. So when Crache-à-Pic's schooner finally came in to dock — swift, clean, relieved of every last jug on the high seas, and bearing a Céleste as superb as the full moon and a Dagobert as radiant as the rising sun — Ti-Louis, Jimmy, and the rest of the Twins had already been waiting since dawn. The first shout was for Céleste:

"Gee, Ma! You look like you swallowed the mast!"

. . . But all eyes were on Adal-Gobert.

There they stood, the pair of them, gasping, eyes full of sea-water, mouths puffed out with words that wouldn't come, meeting again after a hundred years of separation. Clovis claims he heard one say to the other that he'd put on weight.

"But I couldn't say," added the old storyteller, "whether it was Adalbert to Dagobert, or Dagobert to Adalbert."

Well, you can't know everything. . . .

Pushing his wheelbarrow topped with seaweed — with winter coming on I'll bank up my forge like any self-respecting householder, says Old Clovis — a seaweed fresh from the north, from Caraquet to be precise, royally offered to Clovis by his friend Ti-Louis — the old storyteller chews over a mass of thoughts assailing him from the four cardinal points of his brain.

. . . First of all Quicksilver picks up some petty pilferers, apprentice bootleggers who drink from the miraculous grotto and dig up Irish graves. Not much merit in that. Next to nothing for a constable who knows his stuff a little. No reason to go taking himself for Sherlock Holmes. Still, in three months that's more than Martial did in three years.

"Martial, bah!"

. . . After the apprentices, the real thing. This time he catches big game: Black Willy, four big gorillas with their sleeves rolled up over their elbows, a contrabander's vessel, and a complete cargo. A bloody good haul for a young fellow new to the country. Deserves respect. Dieudonné must be chewing his fingernails. And the big boss hasn't seen the end of it yet.

And Crache-à-Pic? Will Quicksilver stop at Dieudonné? Better speak to Ti-Louis and warn him to warn Cap-Lumière that it's never two without three, and that the constable may, from now on, not to say henceforward . . . hmm! . . . better get hold of Ti-Louis the Whistler. The constable must be wondering why she made him that gift of the *Sail Alone* on a silver platter. Everybody must be wondering. I'm wondering myself.

"Come on now, Clovis, there are a thousand reasons. First to mock Dieudonné. And to clear Black Willy and his men out of her road. And then, just for fun, and to show everybody on the coast who the real fox is. And . . . but what if it was to dazzle Quicksilver?"

Quicksilver was also wondering why, how, and thanks to whom, this girl had learned about the new law in the Treaty of Westminster. She was full of the devil, this Crache-à-Pic was. A real stroke of genius. And why? For whose sake? . . . Could it be for his?

Nevertheless, he'd have to catch her too. It was her turn now. The cargo of the *Diable Vert* was stashed safely away, intact, somewhere on his territory. A responsible officer couldn't let that happen.

"Quicksilver will be around digging holes in our back yard for sure," said Crache-à-Pic to her Twins. "I want you to pile cordwood over those barrels and jugs."

For the time being. While waiting to send the whole lot south to the States.

But Quicksilver didn't come digging holes in Cap-Lumière. He had better things to do. He forced Cap-Lumière to stay home. Old Ozite was right: this constable really did have something of quicksilver about him. Everywhere at once and visible nowhere. He spun his web in silence.

This was a new game for Crache-à-Pic, who had been formed in the school of Martial and Black Willy. This man wasn't like the others. It was nerve-racking, this quiet self-assurance of an adversary who sat outside the door of your home keeping a watch on all the exits. Quicksilver was laying siege to Cap-Lumière. Well then, nothing to do but wait.

She's waiting, he told himself. Waiting for me to make the first move. She's not so dumb, the little lady . . . and not so little either. The others aren't fit to tie her shoelaces. The proof is that trick she played with the Treaty of Westminster.

And Quicksilver felt overwhelmed with gratitude to

this girl who had drawn the bear into his trap with a single stroke.

. . . Meanwhile, never awaken the sleeping bear, Crache-à-Pic said to herself, even if he's only pretending. Let him doze quietly on our doorstep and he'll end up looking somewhere else for an instant, and a single instant is all I need. During that short distraction. . . .

But Quicksilver didn't sleep and wasn't to be distracted. He continued to watch all the doors and sideroads, day and night. And Crache-à-Pic stayed in and took out neither truck nor *Sea-Cow*, not even a cartload of hay or marsh grass, not till the snow fell. And with the first snows it was goodbye to the road to Madawaska or the American border till next spring. Now Quicksilver had all winter to carry out his search of Cap-Lumière.

. . . Hmm! . . . A regular giant, this new constable, a man whose likes hadn't been seen in this country since Grandfather Crache-à-Pic, the old ancestor buried under the apple tree and guarded by a bear. . . . The sorcerer's granddaughter struck her forehead. Old Crache-à-Pic's grave! Guarded by a bear who would soon be rolling himself up into a fur ball to hibernate!

That day, while Quicksilver continued his siege around Cap-Lumière, within the walls there were great comings and goings of Twins, Jimmy-the-Flea, and Ti-Louis the Whistler, rolling barrels and carrying bottles to the hole at the foot of the apple tree. At dusk Tobie proudly returned with his bear on a leash, having taken him for a last walk in the woods before his winter's sleep. He surely deserved to see the forest again for a bit, Crache-à-Pic had said to her young brother. And after that they tied him up to the apple tree and promoted him to guardian of the Crache-à-Pic treasure, and of their ancestral spirits.

The year that ended in disaster for Dieudonné saw Quicksilver and Crache-à-Pic equal on points. It was a stand-off. A tie. Old Clovis was tempted to stir the fire, to push them into taking up the combat again, on another level — but he wouldn't have been able to tell you which. Lower than the forehead, higher than the waist. The confrontation of two forces that attract and repel each other instinctively, but whose very contact strikes sparks that spatter the countryside.

"Don't you think we ought to begin the new year with a few fireworks?" Old Clovis asks, winking at his friend Little-Next-to-Nothing.

And Little-Next-to-Nothing claps his hands. Clovis's schemes always make him happy, so he trusts the forge implicitly.

"Go tell your mother to tell Céleste that on New Year's Eve Clovis is going to have a good fire in the forge and tell stories nobody's ever heard before."

Little snot-nose claps his hands again.

"And tell her to say he's going to invite Quicksilver, on account of because it's not Christian to leave a stranger to celebrate New Year's all by himself . . . Céleste can ask anybody she likes from Cap-Lumière, as far as that goes. Do you think you can remember everything I said this time?"

Little-Next-to-Nothing had learnt a lot in a year. He didn't forget a thing. And he took care not to mix up Long-Tongue with one of the Three Kings, or Céleste with Célestine. So on New Year's Eve storyteller Clovis stoked up a good fire in the forge.

First to come in were Melchior, Gaspard, and Balthazar, as pompous as kings; then Céleste and her son Jimmy-the-Flea, accompanied by the Twins; Clovis's daughter Agnès and his daughter-in-law Jeannette just happened to be passing by with a kettle of chicken stew; and finally Quicksilver himself who came in without ceremony to shake hands with the master of the house . . . Thank you, Clovis! . . . and of course Ti-Louis the Whistler, seated on an upturned pail and accompanying every entrance on the harmonica.

Several times Old Clovis got up on the pretext of poking the fire and peeked through the crack in the door, peering out to the horizon . . . I'd never have believed the stubborn thing wouldn't come. . . . Then he'd go back to his place in front of the fire and pick up the thread of his story. Great stories, brand new ones too — as old as Methuselah but new to the ears of the folk on the coast, who heard most of their tales through Clovis.

At five minutes to midnight he excused himself. A man's got a right to take a pee, hasn't he? Got to pee out the bad blood of the old year, he said, stepping into the night.

The Three Kings took advantage of his absence to crack some dirty jokes; the harmonica player to change key; Quicksilver to try to squeeze a word out of each of the Twins; Céleste to defend the Twins against what she considered an invasion of their privacy; Jimmy-the-Flea to tell his mother to . . . but Jimmy's words of advice never reached Céleste's ears, or anyone else's, for the door swung open and a puff of wind blew in an old fellow covered from head to foot in a white fur, bent double down to his knees and walking on his beard. After him came a youngster, almost stark naked, whipping the old man with a switch and shouting in a baby-voice,

"Get out, Old Year! Make way for the New Year!"

And Little-Next-to-Nothing whipped and shouted and played the role his master Clovis had taught him with his whole heart. His mother, Maria, ran after him trying to cover this shivering New Year with a buffalo robe, to the laughter and applause of the guests and the cries of the Old Year, who puffed and panted and finally collapsed in his rags. Seeing this inert form, Céleste, who hadn't got the hang of theatre, rushed to get the vinegar, but opening the Old Year's mouth she heard him croak,

"You'll remember me . . . you'll remember I wasn't a year like the others."

And he collapsed again on the hard-beaten floor of the forge.

Tobie couldn't get to sleep that night, for Céleste had announced that the whole of Cap-Lumière was going to welcome in the New Year over at Old Clovis's forge. But on learning they were also going to welcome in the representative of the law, Crache-à-Pic bawled her out, calling her a gossip-monger, a news-pedlar, a Judas, and a two-faced sell-out to the devil. Céleste retorted that at her age she had the right to sup at whatever bowl she liked and to sit on the bench of her choice; that in years gone by Clovis had been an intimate friend of her late husband; and that Quicksilver would turn his nose up at the invitation, just you wait and see, and scarcely do more than drop by the forge to say how-d'ye-do. The real truth was that Céleste had already tasted Agnès's stew and was licking her chops in anticipation. As for the Twins. . . .

"The only way to get Crache-à-Pic to come is to go on ahead first," one suggested to the other.

For they both knew Crache-à-Pic was dying to go to the forge that night.

She was dying to, but she resisted.

"So what would we do over at the forge, Tobie? We

can rhyme off all Old Clovis's stories on our fingertips. Try to go to sleep."

But Tobie didn't sleep. It was New Year's Eve and Ti-Louis would be playing the mouth-organ and Clovis would tell the story of the sorcerer Crache-à-Pic, the ancestor from the Old Country. . . .

. . . The ancestor's story? He'd tell that before a stranger?

Clovis told it, right from the beginning. He told the story of the greatest sorcerer and giant the coast had ever known, who had triumphed over the Church, the law, and nature itself by heaving up out of his own tomb exactly one year to the day after he had been buried, and who had then changed himself into a will-o'-the-wisp to remind the world that. . . .

. . . The door of the forge opens and they all think they see the hurricane of sorcerer Crache-à-Pic blow in . . . but it's only a gust of wind and a puff of snow whirling around two heads red with cold.

"Jesus, Mary, and Joseph!" exclaims Clovis jumping to his feet. "I think we've got company."

And he runs to close the door behind Tobie and his sister, who were trying to sneak in on tiptoe.

The Twins smile without seeming to; Céleste, who hasn't forgotten the Judas and sell-out to the devil, pouts and won't recognize anyone; Maria, who for the last hour has had eyes for no one but the tall officer with the bushy eyebrows, pretends not to notice that an intruder has come in and goes on rocking her sleeping child. The rest of the forge is suddenly as still as stone before this new apparition.

It's Ti-Louis the Whistler who improvises a completely new tune to set the weathercock upright again and keep the world from collapsing. He really lets go, jumps an octave at a time, switches from minor to major, makes the notes cascade until they all pass their hands through their hair and unwrinkle their brows. Even Céleste finally goes over to Tobie to unwind his scarf and call him a no-good thing who'll never learn to tie his boots right. Maria caresses the tousled head of her little Eugène, who has changed dreams with the music. And at the very moment the master of the forge invites the Three Kings to move over and make room, it's Quicksilver himself, the chief guest, who gets up and offers his chair to Crache-à-Pic.

"We've just buried the old year," he says.

And he offers his hand.

A hand with knuckles as knotty as the roots of a tree, thinks Crache-à-Pic. If only he'd show his palm, you could read the lines in it.

"And paradise at the end of your days," she says, feeling the veins in her fingers swell.

Then she fishes around in her memory for the rest of the formula, only to realize that she has begun with the end and has jumped right over "A happy New Year. . . . " Too bad for the constable. She won't say it over. Since when do you wish your enemies happiness? She takes in the whole forge with a sweep of her head.

"Happy New Year to everyone on the coast," she says.

And she smiles at Quicksilver as if to say: There, do what you like with that! But she can read his smile in reply, saying: I'll keep it for future reference.

About two in the morning the storyteller's chair passed from Old Clovis to Quicksilver. Tell us a story, they said, it's your turn.

So he took his turn.

... At the very beginning of the history of the world, at the time when lions talked to snakes and all the housewives in the land did their Monday-morning wash with the blue of the rainbow, a terrible accident befell the earth. Lucifer had stirred up his fire too much and the lid of the pot blew off. The centre of the globe got so intensely hot that the earth's crust broke out in swellings and blisters that sweat salt water. Until at last the skin dried up and cracked into wrinkles, and out of the cracks leaked some of Lucifer's brew, first in what they called streams, then in rivers. And that's how the sea was born.

Crache-à-Pic was expecting Quicksilver to talk about his own past and his life in Newfoundland. But she didn't at all mind him tracing his ancestors back to the beginning of the world. She just hoped that the night would last, that the first rays of the sun would not come and destroy the charm of the story before its end. She hoped he'd have enough time to bring it up to the present. . . .

... The sea took in all the water that rushed down the hills and mountains, until three-quarters of the earth's crust was covered by oceans. Many animals perished in the flood, and many men, women, and children. The only survivors were the beasts clever enough to grow gills instead of arms and legs, and to learn to swim and breathe under water. Our ancestors came from those fish . . . they were directly descended from the sea turtles who learned how to walk on the sand, then live in the woods, then climb trees, stand on their hind legs, peel bananas, and shell lobsters with their fingers.

Old Clovis had stopped drawing on his pipe. This was a story he didn't know . . . but he'd remember it, never fear, and would be able to pass it down with fifty-six variations. Go on, Quicksilver. . . .

. . . The years stretched into centuries, but men never completely forgot the time when they were fish and sea turtles. That's why so many of them are still drawn by adventure on the high seas and beyond, even today. And that's also why so many people live on islands or on the coast, though life there is more difficult — because they were among the last to leave the water and change their gills back to arms and legs. The men of that race still have rougher voices, and the women smoother skins. And they all speak a language that's just a touch salty . . . !

The forge burst into laughter to break the tension. And none too soon, for the spell was such that the lid of the pot was in danger of blowing off again, and the crust of the earth breaking out in blisters once more.

But they still hadn't had enough of it. Tobie was swimming happily in his primeval past, hunting the depths of the seas for the Crache-à-Pic line clamped to some submarine rock or seaweed; Ti-Louis the Whistler raced ahead of the storyteller elaborating, extending, and enlarging the story in all sorts of ramifications, hoping one of them might seize him, son of a son of the sea, and launch him on the grand adventure of his life; the Twins turned their pointed noses in Crache-à-Pic's direction, while she looked nowhere in particular, for her eyes were turned inward as she tried, stubborn thing that she was, to read the secrets of her heart.

But the rough voice of the storyteller reaches her even there, and forces her to raise her eyes. Now he's talking about man's struggle with the raging sea; about his battles with whales, those reincarnations of ancient sea-dragons; and about his eternal quest for the last word on the mystery hidden at the other side of the horizon, the word no one has ever brought back from his travels.

"And whoever finds that word," says the storyteller,

"will never tell it to anyone else, but will carry it with him to the Islands of No Return . . . those islands everyone catches a glimpse of from time to time, in a mirage, and reaches for with outstretched arms, tempted yet shivering with fear."

Crache-à-Pic discovers that she has stretched out her arms, as if trying to protect this man from a shadow that for an instant cast its profile on the walls of the forge. Then she withdraws into herself, hardens her face, and avoids looking towards Adal-Gobert.

Just as all his listeners hoped, Quicksilver's story stretches out until morning, populating the forge with flora and fauna never before imagined, bringing to life heroes dreamt of since the beginning of time and throwing them into adventures that would console humanity for the loss of paradise.

At first light the Three Kings and the Galoshes come out of the forge reeling happily, drunk with dreams, and feeling tender and grateful towards creation for not having lost them on the long road from the primeval sea to Sainte-Marie-des-Côtes.

But on the doorstep Quicksilver turns towards the men and says,

"What the devil made us forget the oldest tradition of New Year's Eve?"

They all stop and scratch their heads.

"Where I come from, it's the custom to kiss the girls on New Year's Eve."

The Three Kings don't have to be asked twice. Nor Clovis. Not even the youngsters Jimmy-the-Flea and Ti-Louis. Only the Twins remain bashful, their four arms dangling and intertwined. As for Tobie, he lets himself get caught first by Céleste, then by Maria, then by Crache-à-Pic; she has a great need to unload her heart on someone, so she hugs her brother fit to smother him. Then, just as she approaches Adal-Gobert — who manage to blush even in the dawn's early light — she glances between their two heads and catches sight of Quicksilver greedily kissing that whore Maria on both cheeks. And instead of a New Year's kiss, the Twins feel their captain's nails sink into their necks.

The snow has stopped, the wind has fallen. All that remains of the night are five or six ragged stars and Old Clovis waving from the doorstep of the forge, which stands out against the sky like the house of Puss-in-Boots. Crache-à-Pic grabs her brother's hand and tries to draw him away from this night that's all too. . . . But she is swept up, surrounded and swallowed whole in the rough cloth of a peajacket that smells of salt and tobacco. She hasn't time to struggle, or even to wonder if she should struggle, so she lets her heart melt like honey and run through her veins like lightning. Quicksilver's lips are planted on her cheeks, then slip down to the corner of her mouth, which lets out a brief cry muffled in a sigh that Quicksilver accepts as the New Year's greeting she refused him earlier.

"Happy New Year!" he murmurs, peering into the depths of her eyes.

Crache-à-Pic would like to reply but she can barely whisper,

"And paradise. . . ."

The next day the captain summoned her Galoshes and urged them to be more vigilant than ever.

"Winter's just begun, that leaves plenty of time for a sly fox to prepare his first spring appearance," she said.

It was a long winter. But hardly long enough to calm the hot blood coursing through the constable's veins. A sly fox, she had said. The sly fox might have dealt Dieudonné a death blow, and forced all the petty bootleggers playing Robin Hood with other people's business to hole up in their fathers' barns and attics, but he hadn't made a single breach in the invisible wall that encircled Cap-Lumière.

Of course Quicksilver knew all about the cargo of the *Diable Vert* hidden on Crache-à-Pic land. But that was it — the land belonged to the Crache-à-Pics, that race of sorcerers who could blow up a hurricane right out of the tomb. . . . Now don't go thinking the officer was afraid. Not him! Not the man from Saint-Pierre and Miquelon. He was . . . showing respect, that's what it was. Respect for the Crache-à-Pic line. He wasn't going to go hacking up their land. If he did have to stick his pick in some day, he'd only dig in one place. And he had the whole winter to find the right place. He would show Crache-à-Pic that in future the game was to be between the two of them. Like a true gentleman, he would even let her choose the time and place. But he was as determined to win as she was.

. . . Two wild beasts, sighed Clovis. Spying on each other from either side of the snake fence and waiting for spring. And meanwhile both hugging their arms to their chests to keep their hearts from flying away. A long winter in which both constable and outlaw came to forget the law the one had sworn to uphold, the other to defy, both struggling to save their runaway hearts.

"This spring," bragged Crache-à-Pic to gain self-assurance, "we'll scoot between his legs right out to one of Al Capone's ships."

How do you like that! If the Pope turned to bootlegging, this woman would steer straight for Rome in a jiffy. The days of ghosts on the end of a string or nunnies in a rumble-seat were long past. Now the smuggleress had something to prove to someone. And she was spitting fire.

So was Quicksilver — but in silence. For the stranger had no gang to talk to. Not counting the forge, he'd never set foot in a single home on a friendly basis, on this coast that prided itself on being the most hospitable in the county. Hospitable? Sure they were hospitable. But Quicksilver was a constable.

He did get to chat with Clovis, who always did what he wanted anyway, and usually in opposition to everyone else. And through Clovis he talked to Ti-Louis the Whistler, who had no prejudices and plenty left to know about his own origins. Quicksilver, who was eager to learn about everyone's origins, got Clovis talking again about the times of sorcery, the devastating hurricane, and the battle between Old Crache-à-Pic and the *curé*.

"Clovis, is it true they buried the sorcerer under an apple tree?"

"As true as I'm sitting here. And in his place in the cemetery, in a coffin lined with quilted satin, they buried a hardwood log — believe it or not."

And Clovis made the sign of the cross on forehead, mouth, and throat to reinforce his words.

Between the notes of the mouth-organ and the buzzing of a few wakeful flies, the man from Saint-Pierre and Miquelon let drop an insignificant little phrase, hardly worth Clovis's spittoon.

"To bury a giant like that there must have been a pretty fair-sized hole under that tree."

"A fair-sized hole? I'll say it was."

Clovis had said it. Too late now. He'd have preferred to have said nothing, but . . . too bad. The only way to make someone forget a word is to cover it with bigger ones, and more of them. So Clovis began to babble.

"Don't forget, that old sorcerer crawled out of there a year later changed into a werewolf, call it a hurricane if you like. And since that day, believe you me, all that's left in the Crache-à-Pics' yard is the roots of that apple tree, a tree that gives the best McIntoshes in the country every fall. You know the McIntosh? I'll ask my daughter Agnès to bring you over some of her jelly. Every year Tobie takes her three bushels of apples. . . ."

Tobie! Holy Virgin! What a time to be talking about Tobie! It was just a step from Tobie to the bear, a step this canny constable would take in no time. . . . Clovis, shut up!

And that's how the officer came to learn, once he'd visited Tobie in his smelt-fishing shack on the ice of the bay, that the bear hibernated all winter long under the apple tree.

"Under the apple tree!" Quicksilver exclaimed.

"It's his nest," Tobie explained. "Mustn't wake him up before the snow melts."

"Oh, is that so? Not before the snow melts. . . ."

"On account of because in springtime a bear wakes up, you see."

He did.

"As soon as it gets warm, I'll untie him from the tree and take him out to the woods for the whole day."

"To visit his family?"

Tobie's innocent eyes grew big. The idea that his bear might have a family took him back to New Year's Eve. He drooled for joy.

Quicksilver resisted the temptation to push his investigation further. Asking a backward child, Quicksilver, aren't you ashamed of yourself? Anyway, he knew enough already.

It was Crache-à-Pic who continued the questioning, that same night. Quicksilver had visited Tobie on the ice, had he? And talked to him about the bear? And the apple tree? Then he knew. He was crafty, this constable, and quick on his feet. Not the stuff Martial was made of. Here was an adversary who played clean and hard. He hadn't torn up her yard, as he had a perfect right to. He'd taken his time, studied the lay of the land, and done his digging inside his head. Good figuring, that.

"But he still has to come and get it."

And to the Twins she turned a face that reminded both of her double lineage: Crache-à-Pic, and the beautiful Aglaé.

Once he'd heard the news from Ti-Louis the Whistler, Old Clovis ran from the forge to Cap-Lumière, then over to Quicksilver's place, then back to Cap-Lumière, then over to the statue of Saint Joseph and shook his fist at it.

"I'll never believe you'll stay out of things this time."

... Thirty cases of whisky and three barrels of rum, is that worth risking your neck for?

Then Clovis kicked himself. ... Listen, you old jackass, you know damn well it's ages since anyone fought for rum and whisky. You know damn well there's more than liquor down that hole under the apple tree. It's the soul and ashes of Old Crache-à-Pic that's down there, Clovis. Crache-à-Pic who's decided to live again in his descendants, whether you like it or not. Didn't I say as much, the day I saw young Tobie bringing that bear out of the woods? Didn't I say the old sorcerer hadn't said his last word yet, for all he's been dead these thirty years?

Quicksilver might have been listening to Clovis's private reflections, for on squaring off with the beast and seeing that mass of muscles, jaws, and claws, those intelligent eyes and that sensitive nose, the first thing he did was take off his shirt and throw it aside. It was Melchior who saw him.

Clovis said afterwards that Melchior wasn't even on the scene at the start of the combat. But on the day itself nobody was in a mood to contradict the King, or anyone else for that matter. All eyes were on Quicksilver. If he was cold with fear he didn't show it; he walked over to Cap-Lumière with a firm step without looking right or left, without even looking towards the Crache-à-Pics' windows, or Céleste's or the Twins' either. He took the shortest route, marched straight up to the fence, jumped it without touching the fencepost, then stopped thirty feet from the apple tree — just the length of the chain that attached the bear to the trunk.

Clovis didn't know who to keep his eyes on. The bear? Quicksilver? Or on the Crache-à-Pics' house, standing out against the sky like a besieged fortress? He could hardly hold back his friend the Whistler, who wanted to throw himself between the man and the beast.

"Try to understand," Clovis repeated to him, "it wouldn't do any good. That man there isn't fighting against a bear. Try to understand."

But Ti-Louis couldn't. He had to help Quicksilver, to protect him against his madness. Get the Twins out, and Jimmy, and the Three Kings. Send Tobie to calm the beast down. Send somebody to talk to Crache-à-Pic.

"It wouldn't do any good. Put yourself in his skin."

Oh no! Anything but that! At this particular moment Ti-Louis had no desire to be in Quicksilver's skin. Though he'd be ready to join him, along with all the others, and fight by his side.

"Shh! Have a look at the window without turning your head . . . the window of the south dormer."

A shadow. She's there.

She has finally managed to calm Tobie down. . . . Quicksilver just wants to play, we'll have to let him. He won't hurt the bear, I promise you, Tobie; he just wants to test his strength, to see which of them is smartest. A bear is cunning, the man knows that. And very strong, besides. But everyone has his weak spot, you just have to find it. The proof is that the bear let himself be led out of the woods by you, Tobie, by a harmless child.

The Twins are on their front porch, welded together as mute and motionless as temple guardians. But over in one corner, leaning up against a post, Clovis notices a harpoon that used to belong to whale-hunting ancestors.

Suddenly the silence is broken. Céleste has just come out on her porch. She yells and waves and calls for Tobie. . . . Where's Tobie? Where can he be? But Tobie is huddled in his sister's skirts while she repeats to him that everything is all right, Quicksilver is as strong as a bear, and as cunning as a bear, and as brave and true and generous as a bear . . . he'll make out all right, you'll see, and besides, that's grandfather's grave under the apple tree, and he'll be able to recognize a man after his own heart. . . . Don't worry, Tobie, don't worry. . . . Don't worry, Crache-à-Pic.

Ti-Louis tugs at Clovis's sleeve. Quicksilver has just spread his arms on the grass: a shovel, a sledge hammer, a. . . .

"A crowbar!" gulps the Whistler. "I thought he wasn't going to kill him?"

"Shh!" says Old Clovis, trembling. "He must have a plan."

He does. Keep quiet, Clovis! Nobody move! Now he's taking something out of his coat pocket. . . . He's speaking to the bear, who isn't growling, isn't nervous, but is pulling on his chain and making the new leaves on the apple tree shiver. Now Quicksilver is pouring some kind of thick oil on the grass.

"Is he going to set fire to it?"

"Shut up . . . wait and see. . . . It's not oil, it's maple syrup. Look at the bear licking his chops."

A large golden patch spreads out in the grass under the muzzle of the greedy, vicious beast . . . no Clovis, not vicious, you're talking nonsense, just drooling. A good way to catch a bear, Quicksilver, bravo! The bear is licking the grass around his paws, stretching the chain tight about two feet above the ground. . . . Now what's our fine fellow going to do?

. . . Who's that coming?

. . . The Three Kings. Make them shut up!

Quicksilver has left the bear now and is moving off at a distance, figuring things out. The chain is about thirty feet long. That makes sixty feet in diameter with the centre at the apple tree, that's the bear's range. You'd have to be pretty brave to venture into it. Yet the hole is inside, at the foot of the tree. . . . Hurry up, Quicksilver! Soon the bear will have licked the grass right down to the roots. . . . But he's nobody's fool, you'll never get me to believe he's going to go digging with a shovel in a wild animal's territory. . . . Shut up! He must know what he's doing.

He picks up the sledge hammer and the crowbar, an iron stake with a flattened head; then he goes around the tree, comes up on the bear from behind, and approaches within ten feet of him. The bear doesn't turn around. . . . Quiet now! He sticks the stake through one of the links of the chain and . . . pow! The bear feels the shock and lifts his head . . . pow! The bear rears up on his hind feet . . . pow! The bear has just realized that someone is playing around in his yard . . . pow! If you think you're going to get away with that, little man! And he charges.

"Get out, Quicksilver!"

The shout goes up from the four corners of Cap-Lumière. Quicksilver must have heard it. Yet he hasn't taken his eyes off the animal. All he asked was the time for four blows of the sledge hammer. In four blows he has driven the stake home. . . . Back off, Quicksilver! Let's hope that crowbar holds! The bear is checked at the end of his chain, now shortened by two-thirds. That's a dirty trick to play on him, but good going! And the bear has to settle for pacing around the stake and growling in surprise, shame, and indignation.

In three shovelfuls Quicksilver unearths the first jug of the best Caribbean rum from sorcerer Crache-à-Pic's grave, and holds it up at arm's length like an enemy flag.

Whereupon, from the porches, barns, and fences of Cap-Lumière, a shout goes up that astounds Quicksilver. At that moment he is taller than the apple tree; he is a giant with wings on his heels. He can quit the enemy territory freely now; he has won. So, walking around the bear, he goes quietly to his friend Clovis and hands him the trophy.

"Cider," he says, in the most neutral tone in the world. "That apple tree there is a regular still."

And he strides off down to the sea leaving the thirst-ridden inhabitants of Cap-Lumière to joyfully celebrate the victory of man over beast.

"Hee-hee!" laughed centenarian Clovis many years afterwards. "Not the victory of man over beast, but of love over habit and custom. In leaving the merrymakers something to party with, to remember these glorious years of Prohibition all their lives long, he was really inviting the whole country to celebrate the forbidden love-match of a constable and an outlaw."

No one will ever dare say for sure how Crache-à-Pic and Quicksilver spent the rest of the day and the night, but from behind her curtain Ozite saw them take off on the *Sea-Cow* and make for the open sea.

It would take a devil of a smart person to dare criticize Old Ozite or Clovis, or even Ti-Louis the Whistler, who that night composed a jig on his harmonica that's still played at weddings around here.

"Ah, what a wonderful time that was," Old Clovis sighed thirty years afterwards. "Too bad the weathercock had to wake up and start spinning around like crazy again."

CHAPTER FIVE

MIND YOU, THE WEATHERCOCK DIDN'T WAKE UP RIGHT away. All summer long it pretended to be staring at the sun and sat there absentmindedly, its wings outstretched over the coast. But Clovis wasn't taken in. Like anyone native-born he knew how to distinguish a calm sea from a calm at sea. There's nothing more deceptive than the calm before the storm.

"Which means to say, a weathercock sitting there without ruffling a feather doesn't fool me in the slightest."

But that spring and summer of 1932 it fooled Sainte-Marie-des-Côtes and its thirty-six hamlets into thinking that the *Sea-Cow* was sailing head over heels in the clouds. After what had happened under the apple tree, anything was possible . . . anything except seeing Marie-Pet miss Sunday vespers to follow the tracks of that forbidden love through the sand dunes or the slime of the swamps. Every day dawned with "Dear God, is it possible?" and closed with "God help us, it is!"

But as for God, He stayed up there where He belonged and didn't seem in any hurry to interfere. And anyway, even if He'd wanted to. . . .

"Hold your tongue, father. That's enough of your blasphemies."

And daughter-in-law Jeannette slammed the screen

door like a whip. When the weather was good there was too much to do in the fields and the barn and down the rows of the vegetable patch to go running around trying to catch a bunch of bootleggers. That was what Long-Tongue Médard and Annie from the presbytery said too, when they came back home out of breath every night.

But while the whole countryside was eagerly following them, one half crying scandal and the other jumping for joy, Crache-à-Pic and Quicksilver were minding their own business. Two sorts of business that were — and this was the devil of it — totally irreconcilable.

For some time now the forge had been wondering if Crache-à-Pic had only turned to smuggling because of Quicksilver. . . . Go on! She was going to sea long before that. Right back in Martial's day . . . can't you remember? . . . way back then she was already skipping around between the legs of the big bootleggers just to make everybody laugh, having a grand time catching them with their pants down before the boggling, delighted eyes of the little people. Just for the fun of it. Then bit by bit she got caught up in the game and began to go overboard.

. . . It wasn't easy to stop after making a clean sweep of the president's cognac, then winning that fight with Dieu-donné's ghost by a knockout, and . . . and then taking the veil under the name of Sister Marie . . . hee-hee-hee! . . . of the Holy Spittle of the Child Jesus . . . ho-ho-ho!

Well, do you want to know what I think?

In Clovis's opinion all those pirouettes, funny faces, and masquerades were just Crache-à-Pic playing to the gallery of people who'd known her since she was born, and who ten years earlier would never have bet on her against a

Dieudonné. That was the real reason for this new smuggling career, according to Clovis.

But ever since Quicksilver had stepped onto the scene, out of the fog one spring morning, the trickster seemed to be trying to defy another giant than Dieudonné.

"Take that dirty trick she played on Black Willy, out at sea."

. . . Still, he had it coming to him, the pirate. If he hadn't attacked the *Sea-Cow* from behind like that, without even giving warning, he wouldn't have spent Christmas in jail.

. . . Whether he deserved it or not, Black Willy's humiliation was a personal gift from Crache-à-Pic to the new constable. She'd handed the coastguard the *Sail Alone* all tied up in ribbons.

"Did Quicksilver ever thank her for it?"

. . . He took it as a warning. She's telling me the kind of stuff she's made of, he said to himself.

"I see it as more of a challenge, to see if he'd pick it up."

He'd picked it up all right — the next spring, at the ancient sorcerer's grave. Picked it up so well that afterwards Crache-à-Pic fell exhausted straight into her enemy's arms.

"Her enemy!" jeered the wizened little old man hunched up in the corner of the forge.

And everyone understood.

. . . An enemy you abandon to the claws of a bear isn't just an enemy. Crache-à-Pic would have jumped down from her dormer window in a flash to step between the bear and any dolt or braggart who ventured out under the apple tree . . . including a Marie-Pet or a Dieudonné. When a woman lets a man face a danger like that all alone, she has her reasons . . . reasons beyond the reach of reason.

"And if Quicksilver was bold enough to step out under that apple tree . . . could it be that he knew what those reasons were?"

Clovis looked around the circle of heads and scratched his Adam's apple.

"I know some who settle for walking on their hands or splitting a log with a single blow of the axe — that's how my Arthur carried on when he was courting Jeannette. But that sort of behaviour wouldn't have cut any ice with Crache-à-Pic. A man who presents his naked breast to the most ferocious, crafty, and courageous beast nature has ever made doesn't need to go around standing on his head the next day under the windows of eligible young females."

Well, hardly! No sooner had Quicksilver stepped out of the arena than he made straight for the *Sea-Cow*, and went on board and took over the tiller without waiting for an invitation. He knew she would join him there. And to make sure she came alone he had tossed bait to the whole village gathered round the tree, enough to distract them for the rest of the night. Just as he had distracted the bear for an instant with the maple syrup.

She stops on the dock, at the foot of the gangway, breathless and dishevelled. Then she lifts her head and looks towards the barns, to get her breath back and catch the weathercock's eye. And the weathercock winks.

. . . It's your schooner, Crache-à-Pic. I don't see why you'd have to wipe your feet before going on board.

I don't see why either, she says, it's my schooner. She buttons up her pea-jacket, winds a halyard hanging loose around her hands . . . who left that loose, anyway? . . . takes a run, and springs up to the fo'c's'le lithe as a cat. She turns her head from port to starboard, to port . . . nobody? Not a living soul. Nothing. An empty schooner. Huh! . . . Shouldn't expect to find someone on another person's ship at this hour anyway.

She peers at the weathercock again.

. . . You know what they say, the devil always hides in the east.

Crache-à-Pic smiles, pushing back her hair. The devil, sure, but what about archangels?

. . . The moon will be rising very soon. Why not wait for it as you did when you were a kid, sitting cross-legged?

Yes, why not?

She sits down Indian-style, as she used to do when she was small.

. . . Now don't budge. Let time do the rest. Time, her mother Aglaé's favourite weapon. And doubtless Grandfather Crache-à-Pic's too, for he used to say, "Just sit still on your doorstep. . . ."

. . . !

She didn't jump, barely trembled. No Crache-à-Pic was ever afraid of the devil. Yet she felt fingers dig into her shoulders. She has a choice now: she can turn around brusquely and ask the insolent intruder what he's doing on her schooner at nightfall . . . or she can quietly free herself and slowly take in his forehead, his cheeks, his lips . . . or she can sit still, hugging herself, and make the pleasure last.

. . . Store it up, Crache-à-Pic. Bottle it for the long winter nights to come. Your mother had mighty few years to prepare a whole lifetime of winter evenings.

"Were you frightened?"

. . . Frightened of what? Of the devil, or the bear? Just

because a bear likes maple syrup, that's no reason to take him for a dummy. It was dangerous, what you did there — going round the tree like that and entering his territory from behind.

"Weren't you afraid I'd seize your *Sea-Cow* and disappear out to sea?"

She snorts. Afraid for her schooner! And her laughter bounces off the deck like pearls from a broken necklace. At last her throat unknots, and her nerves relax. Her *Sea-Cow*! Her palms caress the smooth wood of this vessel, her confidant and faithful ally for two years.

"Oh, so afraid!" she laughs.

And with her laughter half a dozen words tumble out. Words as old as the language. Words this son of Saint-Pierre recognizes by sound and by touch.

All night long Crache-à-Pic must have repeated those long-reserved words — words she'd never used before, words Old Clovis absolutely refused to repeat to my father — for when dawn broke Quicksilver caressed her lips and murmured,

"I'm going to pick them like wild berries and bottle them for the bad days."

"What bad days?"

"Tomorrow, or the day after tomorrow, when you go back and find an empty space at the foot of your apple tree."

"That hole will never be empty."

"I know."

"How do you know?"

"I know because I walked right over it yesterday."

"And do you think Grandfather's still there?"

"I think the soul of the Crache-à-Pics fills the whole of Cap-Lumière."

"Yet it's you who won under the apple tree."

"I had to win."

"Is the job of a constable so important, then?"

Quicksilver teases her with his hands, his eyes, his teeth.

"If I'd lost to the bear he'd have eaten me whole."

"But nobody sent you out to fight a bear."

"Ah, no?"

She blushes. Then lets her head drop back against his shoulder.

"It's all over," she whispers. "Tomorrow Tobie will introduce you to the bear."

Quicksilver smiles sadly.

"There are stronger things than bears at Cap-Lumière."

Old Clovis was the first to understand that Quicksilver's struggle had just begun. Crache-à-Pic was an outlaw like none other, a thoroughbred. She knew the battle would last; she willed it. And Quicksilver had his own reasons for defending law and order and opposing the smugglers. Nobody ever knew how the old storyteller pried the officer's secret out of him; Quicksilver didn't even tell Crache-à-Pic. And when Ti-Louis tried to make Clovis talk that autumn, the old boy turned away and began to go over Little-Next-to-Nothing for lice.

"Quicksilver is a Martin from Saint-Pierre," he said. "I used to know Martins from the island of Miquelon, same branch, but not cousins."

Ti-Louis the Whistler blinked. His friend's riddles left him gaping but sharpened his wits. Clovis knew this, the old rascal, and laid it on thicker.

"One day," he proclaimed, "someone will have to pay for the sins of others. On account of because nothing under the sun remains hidden from the eye of God. Even if it takes a hundred years. ... "

It only took the coast a summer and an autumn to re-create, around the most famous and primeval couple in all the east, an atmosphere of paradise before the fall: apple tree, and forbidden fruit protected by a wild beast, and Adam and Eve too — whom Long-Tongue Médard swore he had seen between the dunes one night, as naked as worms. ...

"And what were you doing down by the dunes at night, you old billy-goat?" his wife, Alisca, wanted to know.

... And nature too was wild and mad that summer, with wheat growing up in the midst of the oat-fields and ferns sprouting in the gravel in the middle of the King's Highway.

Yet this was far from the first madcap romance that Sainte-Marie-des-Côtes had known. A seaport, a centre for contraband, and a nest of bootleggers, the village was visited by foreign steamers and brigs every year; it was used to hearing its *curé*'s voice calling down the wrath of God. After all, this same country had produced Don l'Orignal, Bolicaille, and the Cordes-de-Bois. What about them, eh? It had seen salmon swim up the rapids, and an oak growing right in the middle of a beech grove. ... But what of it? Do you ever get used to shooting stars, or the northern lights, or the V of wild geese in the sky? Everything that makes you lift your head and squint your eyes, Old Clovis used to say, makes you think.

"Yet it's only a couple of steps between thinking, and grinding your teeth, and sneering."

Ti-Louis made the most of his old friend's meanderings, for Clovis was never more pithy than when he was rambling on about nothing at all. That morning in the forge, for example, commenting on sneering, he got around to distinguishing between the taunting of his daughter-in-law, Jeannette, and the taunting of his pal Melchior. The King's teasing was meant to keep the game going; the daughter-in-law and Marie-Pet were hoping to see the players fall flat on their faces. So the whole country was now shadowing the new lovers, but for different reasons.

"Sooner or later I'll catch them in the act," raged Marie-Pet, forgetting herself and thinking out loud.

"In the act of what?" sneered Melchior.

And the whole forge burst out in a roar of laughter.

But Marie-Pet didn't catch anybody in any act. For this couple from paradise who threw their shadow the whole length of the coast didn't parade their love in front of anyone.

"I hear tell," said Xavier-the-Hunchback one day, "that Marie-Pet is fixing to learn to swim."

"What! At her age?"

"That's a fact. . . . On account of because she's been chasing those lovers so hard through the woods and over the dunes that she's forced them to take to the open sea."

And Xavier leered seaward, licking his lips. The whole country was tempted to lift the fig-leaves and ogle the multiple splendours of original sin. And although not a soul had seen a single thing, it became a contest to see who could boast the most about intercepted indiscretions.

" . . . Yesterday evening, up by Bois-Joli. . . ."

"Jehosaphat! At the same time, yesterday evening, they were washing their feet in the doctor's stream."

"Baloney! I saw them myself going at it like cat and dog, yelling names at each other from either side of the Allains' creek. Call them lovers . . . bah!"

"It's jealousy makes everyone talk so."

"Jealousy! Jealousy? I'll have you know, father, that a Després from Cocagne hasn't a reason in the world to feel jealous of a Crache-à-Pic, as it so happens. And besides, I'm a married woman, and married to your son into the bargain."

"The poor devil! I tried to warn him."

Jeannette would have liked to fly in her father-in-law's face, but she remembered her manners — in matters of manners she was uncompromising. So she restrained herself to a tight squirm of the bum that set the Kings off on the road to Bethlehem.

"Christ Almighty!" exclaimed Gaspard, "if things go on like this, the country's going to have its own Massacre of the Holy Innocents."

Long-Tongue Médard had just let drop into the middle of the forge the news that he'd seen a schoonerful of holy nuns heading out for the open sea.

"What?"

. . . The whole convent not counting the Mother Superior and the old crones, those saints shut up in their cells chewing their prayers three times over — all embarked, would you belie e it, on the *Sea-Cow*. Like it or not, Crache-à-Pic was refining her methods. Nothing could hold out against her coaxing. And since she'd sunk her teeth into the apple of paradise, she was bolder than ever.

"Is the witch going in for piety now? One day she takes the veil and the next she sets off for the missions with a whole community."

'She's got a mission, all right."

"Hold your nasty tongues."

"Lay off them, I say. For once a little rum-running is placed under the protection of Holy Mother the Church and they don't have to fork out a cent for it, let the innocent things have a bit of fun with no risk of getting their habits mussed."

"That's what *you* say, Melchior — without getting mussed! But suppose an officer catches them out at sea and decides to search the ship, and a fight breaks out — those Sisters would learn then and there what the real purpose of the trip was; they'd find out a little tour on a smugglers' schooner is no picnic, and. . . ."

" . . . and the whole thing would end up in the cow-field again! Judas Priest, Long-Tongue! The country would go wild! But there's no danger of things going that far. You know damn well there's not a Quicksilver on the coast would dare arrest a schoonerful of nuns singing *Ave Maris Stella*."

"And if you don't know that, Médard, Crache-à-Pic does!"

And Old Clovis rubbed his thighs with glee.

"I tell you, that Crache-à-Pic will have the last word — over the law, over the other bootleggers, and over that whole lot of snappish, snivelling, fiddle-faddlers who go sticking their noses into her business. She's too strong for. . . ."

" . . . for Quicksilver?"

It's the little hunched-up old gaffer speaking out again.

"Two wild beasts of enemy species," he says. "But of the same race."

"You'll settle down in the end," said the constable.

"Would you like me to be like one of the Babineau girls?"

"It wouldn't be much fun if I had to break into your nest and truss you up."

"I'd know how to start over and make myself a nest elsewhere."

"Then I'd be elsewhere too, hidden in the hay spying on you."

"And the battle would begin again, and I'd win again, too."

"Not every time. Every other time it would be my turn."

"And then?"

"And then I'd make you pay, all night long."

"Until death do us part!"

What a beautiful summer it was! What a magnificent autumn! Enough to keep Marie-Pet and Long-Tongue breathless.

"I'll catch them sooner or later," the old harpy whined to the wild geese.

But that year the grey geese made the most of the sky's uncertainty as it hovered between two seasons.

. . . Soon? The spring goslings asked the mother goose.

And the big goose sniffed the air like the weathercock.

"Just be patient," she answered in her unhurried way. "When the time comes you'll have plenty of time to say it's come too soon."

"Time's dragging," insisted Crache-à-Pic. "I want to take you to the beech woods. I want to show a lad from the isles the real life of the woods."

"Don't rush time, please," Quicksilver sighed. "I knew a time when I pushed at the years like a cart I wanted to make go up the hill faster. Till the day an old man at home told me the name of the cart."

"I know it. It's in an old story told me by Clovis the Elder, father of Old Clovis, when I was five. The Wagon of Death. Now, twenty years later, I've already met it four or five times. It's nearly run over my feet, the bastard! But I've never been afraid of it."

"I've never been afraid of it either," replied Quicksilver. "Not until today."

"Why today?"

He didn't reply but took her in his arms and crushed her to him, almost smothering her.

"We'll catch them in the act yet," repeated the chorus of wagging tongues, while the others cheered this return of an Adam and Eve who were accountable only to God.

Then winter closed in. And in its wake came gales, snowstorms, squalls, incertitudes, moans, and whisperings by the fireside . . . was the government going to let things go to pot for another year? How long before the end of the Depression, of misery, of Prohibition?

"The end of Prohibition! The country's never been better off!"

"Heretics!"

And the discussion took off again, ranging from murmur to abuse to open threats of never again setting foot in a house that deserved to be burnt to the ground.

But it was the depth of winter, and nobody had ever seen forest fires — known as scourges of God — ravage the homes of the heathen in the month of January.

In March the first wild geese came back. They were early. Agnès wanted to know if that didn't mean spring was on its way and if they shouldn't ask the *curé* to advance the blessing of the seed. But Clovis replied that Saint Mark wasn't going to go moving his feast day on account of a few dozen giddy geese and that the liturgical calendar should be respected.

"Too much messing around and we'll end up having Lent in August," he declared.

But the geese didn't appreciate the old scoundrel's

reflections on them, and for the rest of the day they wheeled over his head.

" . . . We'll show you, we'll show you, old mumble-chump!"

To the point where old mumble-chump had to admit,

"Maybe it won't be a spring like the others, after all."

He woke up with a start, under the first April sun. Spring was so swift and bold that it came in wild disorder, with buds bursting at the ends of the branches like roasting chestnuts. An orgy of spring, fit to send everyone in the country ecstatically out into their front yards.

"After a feast like that, all that's missing is the Flood."

Ti-Louis shivered. Why did rain inevitably follow good weather? The earthly paradise that all Sainte-Marie-des-Côtes had re-created to shelter the love of Crache-à-Pic and Quick-silver — would it too fall victim to the first big storms of April? And then what would happen to this love affair, abandoned to the tender mercies of that spiteful clan?

Ti-Louis tormented himself over this without daring to bother Clovis or his aunt Célestine about it. He had yet to tell anyone of his hopeless passion for Crache-à-Pic, his first adolescent love, stronger than winter, more fragile than summer. He stood no chance himself, but perhaps with his sword of fire he could guard the gates of paradise against intruders.

One morning, pushing his friend's wheelbarrow — for Clovis has decided it's high time to make up for lost time — the young man begins blathering about rain and fine weather and strewing his speech with ambiguous, enigmatic phrases such as: Ah well, what can you expect? . . . They'll be saying a little rain settles a strong wind. . . . Pull up the weeds and you pull up the good grain too. . . . . Rainbow at night, sailor's delight. . . .

Clovis raises an eyebrow — the left one, the one for questioning — and casts a searching look at his talkative young friend. Then he decides to take the bull by the tail, just for fun.

"Seems the Allains' Maria still hasn't forgiven Crache-à-Pic."

Ti-Louis's head comes up like a spring.

"It's because poor Maria's had her eye on the constable, so they say," continues Clovis, "ever since that famous New Year's Eve."

Ti-Louis bursts out,

"Maria! But you can't compare Maria to Crache-à-Pic. . . ."

And the young man pulls a face like an old connoisseur of the fair sex. But Clovis continues pitilessly.

"Maria's a nice girl," he says, "but the poor creature never had much luck after that accident with the Norwegian sailor. If all the nice girls I know had drawn a wild card one night when the moon was full, the way Maria did, there wouldn't be so many of them turning their noses up at her now."

Ti-Louis blushes, stammers, wrestles with his words. He hasn't got anything against Maria, he's not judging her, that's not the point; and he hasn't got it in for Norway either. He would gladly defend Maria's honour against the whole world if necessary. Just as long as she didn't get it into her head to start competing with Crache-à-Pic. He's ready to recognize every man in the country as his own rival, beginning with Quicksilver, but in his eyes no one holds a candle to Crache-à-Pic. And Clovis hears him mutter between his teeth,

"Maria'd better watch out she doesn't get mixed up in this."

In a country where the weathercock spins the winds willy-nilly and backs them up on themselves, twisting the nor'easter through the masts and then blowing without warning through the cracks of barns and attics, it's really not easy to keep a secret. The least breeze has a trick of making off with words you've barely formulated, and integrating them into the framework of a complex statement.

So it was that the discussion between the two pals stumping along behind that empty wheelbarrow between the piles of a broken-down dock reached all the way to Dieudonné's barn floor. And even though he paid no attention to this prattle from a decrepit blacksmith's shop, big Dieudonné, self-styled Master of the Gulf, began to peer over at the Allains' just the same.

One day he called his faithful Black Willy, who'd sworn when he got out of prison that he'd clean Crache-à-Pic out right to the marrow of her bones, and asked him about the girl Maria.

"Isn't she the mother of that little good-for-nothing who's always hanging around the forge lately?"

"The little snot-nose Eugène-à-Maria," specified Black Willy. He could see a new adventure looming up on the horizon, one that would give him a chance to vent his spleen.

"A kid she had by a passing sailor, so they say?"

"One sailor or another; seems this Maria isn't all that choosy."

Dieudonné was thoughtful for a while.

. . . Not too choosy, eh? . . . Yet Quicksilver isn't what you'd call your average man. . . . If Maria shows an interest in him, she doesn't lack taste, or brass.

"She certainly isn't short on nerve, to take a bite out of the same apple as Crache-à-Pic."

That apple again! Without meaning to, the chief smuggler had referred to the same Bible as all those babblers, chin-waggers, pipe-slurpers, and Monday-morning washerwomen. He too had approached the wall of flames encircling the earthly paradise.

"You'll have to bring this Maria around to see me one of these days, Black Willy."

. . . ?

"Bring her around to the kitchen door. Zéphirine has too much to do since the house got bigger. Maria must know how to mend and polish."

Black Willy let his imagination carry him away across seas and isles to a place where he led the Crache-à-Pic girl into confusion, drowned her, and drew and quartered her, while rubbing his hands with pleasure. But his fingers twisted when he heard his boss add,

"And while you're at it, bring me Jimmy-the-Flea too. Seems that last year he delivered a load of barrels from Caraquet in less time than any of your men, Black Willy."

Maria soon showed Zéphirine and Dieudonné's wife that she knew how to mend, polish, and mind her own business as well. Also that she could perform several tasks at the same time, and take on work that wasn't spelt out in her contract without sulking. For as soon as she set foot in Dieudonné's home, the sailor's girl understood what was required of her. The bootlegger had to get close to the representative of the law and was counting on her to clear the road for him.

"A girl like you," he told her, "mustn't let a guy like that look anywhere else when she walks down the street. Work in closer and closer to his back door."

So Maria grew bolder. Especially since she was getting paid for it.

Black Willy had less luck with Jimmy-the-Flea. According to Clovis, Black Willy was not at all keen on enrolling this young slyboots into Dieudonné's clan. He was quick-witted, a jack-of-all-trades formed in Crache-à-Pic's school, a lively lad with bootlegging in his blood, and one who would surely end up behind the wheel of a Scottish Fisherman one of these days. So while Willy offered Dieudonné's propositions with his right hand, with the left he was counting on his fingers the number of months left until the abolition of Prohibition. He even let slip between his teeth,

" . . . bootlegging's best days are over."

Jimmy-the-Flea was the only one of the Galoshes to scowl and kick against the wall of paradise set up around Crache-à-Pic and Quicksilver. One day he complained to his mother — who told him to go blow his nose — that nobody knew which end was up any more around Cap-Lumière, and if things went on like that. . . .

"If you keep on having cold feet I'll take over the helm of the schooner myself, and you can take my place and feed the chickens every morning."

Next Jimmy turned to the Twins, and by chance let fall the suggestion that Adalbert could very well take charge of *Saint Anthony's poor-box* this spring while Dagobert took over the *sponge in the holy-water font*, and then Jimmy-the-Flea would take the *Sea-Cow* out to the islands. . . . With that the apprentice committed a double error, first in separating the Twins, then in setting himself up as captain of the schooner that was the sole creation and property of Crache-à-Pic. Adal-Gobert let the young numbskull know that the day he went out to sea without Crache-à-Pic's knowledge, he'd end up drowned in the drink. After which Jimmy told nobody else what was on his mind, but started taking out his resentment on Tobie.

Twice that harmless boy had to go running through the fields to the edge of the woods in search of his escaped bear. But he didn't catch on, so he lit into the poor animal and accused him of untying himself.

"Don't you know you're not supposed to do that, bear? If Crache-à-Pic gets hold of you. . . ."

But Crache-à-Pic, quicker and more perceptive than her brother, instead got hold of Jimmy-the-Flea, the real culprit. She had a high regard for the bear's intelligence and knew he was capable of a thousand tricks — but not of unfastening the chain all by himself.

"So what's Tobie done that you hold against him, eh Jimmy?"

. . . His grudge wasn't against Tobie, it was against life — and particularly against Crache-à-Pic. So he risked replying,

"Why is it I get the blame every time something goes wrong at Cap-Lumière?"

Then, under his breath:

"Did anyone say anything to a certain person who went and shortened the bear's chain last spring?"

Crache-à-Pic didn't push her interrogation further, she could see it all now. And she decided that in future the Twins should keep an eye on Jimmy-the-Flea. That's how

Adalbert came to be following the young Galosh from a distance when he had his first meeting with Black Willy; and he went and told Dagobert about it at once.

"That smells like Dieudonné, that does."

"Stinks of it."

"Would it be better to talk to Jimmy first, or to tell Crache-à-Pic right off?"

"What would be best?"

"Maybe Céleste. . . ."

"If you go telling Céleste you might as well shout it out to the whole village."

For the Twins the village was Crache-à-Pic, her brother, Jimmy-the-Flea, and Céleste. They weren't socializers, and they didn't go sticking their noses into life outside Cap-Lumière. Yet all Sainte-Marie-des-Côtes respected them. Yes, but the Twins, each with his half-share of wisdom, had learnt to mistrust respect of a popular and collective kind. They realized that a respect based on the mysterious feeds on mystery, so that it was in their interest to stay hidden behind each other as long as possible.

"What if we spoke to Black Willy?" one of them ventured.

The other immediately took over the phrase, to show his brother that he shared it and accepted his measure of responsibility, come what might.

"We ought to speak to Black Willy," he echoed.

And Black Willy never did know which of the two accosted him one evening, just as he was getting into an ambulance upholstered in ten-ounce bottles of rum, and demanded a straight answer—immediately, with no fudging—to his questions.

Black Willy was hot-tempered and didn't appreciate

this type of aggression. He doubled up his fists and was just getting ready to take the offensive himself when he heard the questions coming from another mouth behind him. He turned abruptly only to find himself face to face with the same Twin, who wanted to know what he'd been doing snooping around Cap-Lumière and what his relations were with Jimmy-the-Flea. Swing as he might from port to starboard, Black Willy was surrounded by Twins — identical right down to their bandanas, their crunched-up caps, the gleam in their eyes, the way their heads were cocked, and the way their teeth were clenched. He decided to bargain.

He promised to lay off Jimmy-the-Flea, on condition that Adalbert, or Dagobert . . . whoever it was that wasn't the other one blocking the ambulance's way at that particular moment . . . let him get on with his job and. . . .

"Conditions?" the Twins exclaimed in chorus, approaching Black Willy together, one on his left, one on his right.

Just then the bootlegger remembered one of his boss's bright ideas: Twins are only strong as pair; if you can separate them you'll have them eating out of your hand. He put on an unctuous expression of good will and made his proposition.

"You know as well as I do that Dieudonné hasn't got anything against you. The proof is that airplane ride over the woods. He hasn't got anything against Jimmy either, or Céleste — what's Céleste ever done to him? — or that poor, simple-minded slave of the Good Lord, Tobie. He wouldn't even have it in for Crache-à-Pic if the bitch . . . if Aglaé's daughter would just stay quiet. Dieudonné is ready to forget everything: the Sisters' cows, the retreat house, the *Sail Alone*. . . .

This name stuck in the bootlegger's back teeth, and

he couldn't bring himself to mention the escapade of the false nuns in the States either. The Twins didn't miss his grimace, and they let the orator puddle around and sink up to his ankles in his dishonesty.

But Black Willy freed himself and cast out the big bait.

"Which of you two wants to be the first to go through the tunnel?" he asked.

. . . The tunnel? Dieudonné's secret tunnel? Were the Three Kings' tales true, then, about an underground passage from the bootlegger's barn to . . . ? But the Twins weren't born yesterday and they weren't going to fall into any trap, even a trap as long as a tunnel leading to. . . .

"So where does this tunnel of yours go?"

It was Dagobert who spoke — or it could have been . . . it was the one on the left at any rate . . . at least he was on the left when he asked, but they'd moved since . . . how was it possible to keep track of which one was interested . . . ? Have to find that soft spot again, bring back the instant of weakness. . . .

So, focusing his gaze on the first star to pierce the evening sky, Black Willy again extended his invitation to whichever of the two showed the most curiosity.

"Promise to hold your tongues and I'll take one of you a good quarter of the way across village, underground, on all fours. The other can have his turn after."

"Why not both at the same time?" asked the two voices together.

Black Willy mumbled that it was too dangerous, there wasn't enough light in the hole, Dieudonné never took more than one man at a time, it was take it or leave it.

They'd take it. Just the same, the Twins wanted to know where the second one should wait for the first — in

other words, where the end of the tunnel was. Black Willy
didn't see the catch. But once they were underground, and
halfway between Dieudonné's barn and an abandoned shed
on the property of the late Cyprien, Célestine's father-in-
law, he realized that the Twins had outfoxed him. While
Adalbert crawled along behind Black Willy, who was trying
to tease information out of him, Dagobert entered the tunnel from the other end and quietly crept towards them.
And that's how, in the bootleggers' high command — ten
feet underground — Crache-à-Pic's two most devoted protec-
tors squeezed secrets out of Dieudonné's most faithful
servant.

That same evening Célestine was coming back from Cap-
Lumière, where she had been exchanging the latest news
with her cousin Céleste: Zéphirine had help in the
Dieudonnés' kitchen, the Allains' Maria, believe it or not!
"Maria?"
"Maria!"
"And why Maria!"
"Why Maria?"
"That's what I asked."
"In your place I'd ask Crache-à-Pic."
After this short interchange at Cap-Lumière, Célestine
was coming home across the fields. The moon was high,
and its rays traced a path for her by way of the tackle and
rigging sheds that had belonged to the late Cyprien.
"I've kept them, Father Cyprien, all I sold was the land;
you can rest easy."
Any woman who had to go out alone at night in those
shady years preferred to talk to her deceased relatives rather
than listen to herself breathing.

"Don't you worry, Dieudonné learnt his lesson with those false papers of his; he won't dare come near your buildings or your house. You can rest in peace, Cyprien."

Then she stared, eyes agog. Three shadows preceded by a single lantern were making their way around one of the sheds. Holy Mary Mother of the Infant Jesus! . . . Was the country really haunted, then? A ghost at Hallowe'en, and three devils coming out of the ground at Pentecost! But the Hallowe'en ghost of 1930 had hardened the timorous and sharpened up the credulous; by the spring of 1933 devils had to be mighty smart to draw people to their black sabbaths. So once her surprise had passed, Célestine readjusted her kerchief and chuckled . . . she'd been getting used to devilment like this ever since Black Willy had got out of prison, and especially after all this talk of abolishing Prohibition.

"Ever since those rum-runners began to smell the end in sight, they won't back off anything. Well, this time they're going to back off — right out of my buildings!"

And hitching up her skirts, Célestine marched straight down on the sheds.

Next day the two cousins had to struggle with their consciences for an hour before they could decide, yes or no, whether to speak to Crache-à-Pic. The Twins! Just imagine! Her fine-feathered friends Adal-Gobert making deals with Black Willy, at night, in a shed in the middle of a field! Célestine queried Céleste, who queried Célestine, who put her head in her hands while Céleste shook her fist at the heavens. Sit tight and close-lipped? Or spill the beans and let her rip? That was the question.

But in their hesitation they deliberated so loudly that

Crache-à-Pic ended up knowing everything before the cousins had made up their minds, yes or no.

The smuggleress preferred to keep her feelings to herself. If the Twins had betrayed her, she couldn't trust anyone — not even Céleste and her cousin Célestine. With a disgusted shrug that said, "What difference does it make anyway?" she slipped away.

She went out to the bear, carrying a can of maple syrup. She was alone — alone for the first time since she'd come back to the coast. For when she'd entered port at the helm of the *Sea-Cow* three years ago, at the very first glance she'd picked out Céleste, Jimmy, her brother Tobie (balancing awkwardly on two feet as though standing on one) and, off to one side and soldered together, Adalbert and Dagobert. Her mother's clan had adopted her unconditionally, and had taken her as their captain. At Cap-Lumière the Crache-à-Pics had passed the sceptre on in the simplest of ceremonies for over a century. The investiture of the last of their race had taken place at her mother's bedside:

"Eat all you want of Dieudonné's strawberries, currants, and gooseberries, and don't think twice about it because, remember, he stole those fields from poor folk in the first place."

That day, Crache-à-Pic had known it would be her lot to fight the bootlegger, David against Goliath, armed only with her courage and a cunning that would soon astound the whole country. But she hadn't had to lift a finger to win over the clan of the Galoshes. With one word — her last — Aglaé had shown her daughter to the folk of Cap-Lumière:

"Crache-à-Pic," she said.

The king is dead, long live the king.

But today, for the first time, Crache-à-Pic was confiding her solitude to the bear. If the Twins . . . the Twins who had replaced her own father, who had sworn loyalty to her mother and never went back on their word . . . if the Twins were abandoning her, that meant . . .

" . . . the devil is loose," she said.

The devil at liberty. Crache-à-Pic knew all too well what form the devil had taken at Cap-Lumière this past year. And what a handsome devil he was. How did you live outside paradise after the fall? The love-sick girl didn't think about it, she wouldn't. Her mother had sent her this man on the anniversary of her own death, and Crache-à-Pic saw that as a sign from heaven. The parish could preach hell, purgatory, and limbo all it liked; she knew her mother was in paradise with the angels. Or better still—wherever her mother was, that was paradise. The rest of the celestial cosmos didn't interest Crache-à-Pic.

. . . Can you figure it out, bear? Can you understand anything about men, what makes them so jealous of one another? First it's Jimmy who starts to kick over the traces, and now it's Adal-Gobert. What's got into them all? It rubs them the wrong way to see someone else dare come near me . . . dare. . . . But whatever he does, Quicksilver will never stop me from putting out to sea at night, or from digging my hideouts in the woods, or from spoiling Dieudonné's game. He knows all that, anyway. He knows he could ask me to die and I would—but I'll never do anything to make a single Crache-à-Pic turn in the grave.

The bear has licked up the last drop of syrup, and is now licking his mistress's fingers. She strokes his muzzle, his flanks, his back. Magnificent beast. But it's her man who conquered him. A man of her ancestors' race—the old men of the village saw the resemblance at once. It's this man, with his deep-set eyes, his bushy eyebrows, his arms as knotty as roots, and his thick speech, thick but gentle, it's this man who has opened the fiery gates of paradise for her every day for a year now. . . . And it's this man who has so overturned her life that now, one by one, her Galoshes are disappearing behind a curtain of fog to nurse their invisible resentments.

Suddenly Crache-à-Pic digs her fingers into the bear's coat and tightens them. Ti-Louis the Whistler! She's just thought of her young protégé, almost a brother, the only one among them who hasn't yet taken a dislike to Quicksilver — perhaps the only one pure enough, she thinks, not to be infected by the pain of love.

If she'd only known! sighed Clovis the storyteller.

But for the moment she suspects nothing; she feels she can count on his perfect loyalty, and on the fact that he is too young and innocent to be devoured by jealousy.

She leaves the apple tree and heads for the forge.

"Ti-Louis left early, he's gone fishing," says Old Clovis. "But he shouldn't be long, because he's with the Three Kings and they never go far out."

"So even the musician has taken up poaching now?"

"He just goes along to . . . to play for the others."

Then, looking over towards his spiderweb:

"But if you've got a message for him, Crache-à-Pic, I won't be stirring from here all morning long."

"Mind if I wait, Clovis? From your forge you get a great view of the whole coast."

"Of the whole country for that matter, inside and out."

"If you were Old Ozite, I'd ask you to read the cards for me."

"If I were Ozite I'd show you more kings and jokers than there are in the pack, and you might be surprised."

. . . The little old monkey! He wants to get me talking. Well, I'll see who talks first and longest. And she stares resolutely at the line of the horizon.

. . . So that's it, chuckles Clovis. Hee-hee! Folks from the same country don't have to stand on ceremony. Her heart's too full, poor child, for her to keep silent long. All I have to do is lift the cover of the pot a touch and . . . pssst!

"I don't read cards, but I read teacups," he says, filling a chipped teapot with boiling water.

Then, placing a cup of the same vintage before Crache-à-Pic:

"It's not new, this battered old thing. It was a wedding present to my late missus from her mother-in-law. Napoleon could have taken a cup from it . . . and then my grandfather could have foretold his destiny . . . that would have cooled him down a mite."

"You think so?"

. . . ?

"You think a man who knows what's in store. . . ?"

Then she stops. Better let the old boy mumble on. Clovis pours the tea and smiles broadly.

"Go on, go on, it's not poison. It's the only thing a single man knows how to make in the kitchen, a good cup of tea. . . . Luckily, he knows how to do a thing or two elsewhere, hee-hee! Otherwise no woman would want him."

She can see him coming, and sticks her nose in her cup.

"A man who can make a cup of tea like that," she teases, "hardly needs to know how to brew bathtub beer too."

. . . Well now! There she goes taking a sideroad, the cunning thing. But all roads lead to Rome. I'll catch her yet.

"You were pretty small when your father died?"

"Just three."

"And old Crache-à-Pic your grandfather?"

"I never knew him. But you must remember him well, Clovis. Is it true what the old folks say about him?"

"The hair in his nose, and his handlebar moustache?"

"And his battle with the *curé*, and the hurricane that came up out of his grave. . . . Was he really a sorcerer, or just a man more crafty and knowing than the rest?"

Clovis has been waiting a long time for this question. Sooner or later some shrewd character had to ask. She has a good head, this Crache-à-Pic.

"My girl, your ancestor was the biggest, smartest, hardest-headed cuss that ever walked this coast. We haven't seen another like him in thirty years. The only one who comes close. . . ."

Crache-à-Pic and Old Clovis stare each other down. The same name is burning on both their lips. Whoever utters it first knows it will break the equilibrium the spiders of the forge have spun into their webs in imitation of the web-spinning below.

"Quicksilver and Maria. . . !"

Ti-Louis bursts into the forge. He stops short when he sees Crache-à-Pic, who has stiffened at the constable's name. Then he ceremoniously takes off his cap, blushes, babbles something or other, gulps a mouthful of water from the pump, and tries to find another opener to wipe out the first one.

"Shut that door more quietly than you opened it, if you don't want to wreck my last spiderweb," Clovis suggests. "Then draw up a bench, because there's someone here has something to say to you."

And turning towards Crache-à-Pic:

"Unless that something is none of my business and you prefer to talk elsewhere. . . .You can even do it right here while I go to Marie-Pet's and return that wheelbarrowful of plenary indulgences she gave me to look after the week of the three Thursdays."

All this nonsense to distract Crache-à-Pic from the unlucky words Ti-Louis burst in with. Unlucky all right — it's written all over the poor thing's face. But Crache-à-Pic doesn't intend to be distracted. And how could she? The whole forge is ringing with "Quicksilver and Maria . . . Maria and Quicksilver. . . ." And the spiders go back to spinning like crazy.

When Crache-à-Pic had left the forge's field of vision, Old Clovis seized his friend by the shoulders and sat him down with his back to the fire.

"Now talk," he said.

But poor Ti-Louis's throat was as rough as sandpaper. He finally managed to blurt out,

"That damned Maria, it's the limit. She's gone and sucked Quicksilver right into the bootleggers' barn. It was Médard who saw them."

"Catch your breath and don't rush your words. First off, you say you got your information from Long-Tongue, fancy that! But since when does the forge feed on stories from that pedlar of lies? Are we so short of news we have to stock up from tattletalers? . . . So what did Médard say?"

"With his own eyes he saw Quicksilver going into Dieudonné's barn with Maria."

And, lowering his voice:

"Seems they were holding hands."

"The devils!"

Old Clovis took a deep breath. He shut the only window in the forge, checked that the door was locked, then came over and sat down opposite his friend.

"Ti-Louis, mv boy, are you a man?"

Ti-Lous blinked rapidly.

"Well now, if you're a man, you're going to have to act like a man. You're going to have to have Maria."

This time Ti-Louis didn't blink. His four eyelids were stuck wide open; he couldn't move. Seduce Maria? Him? But he wanted to cut her throat, to break her into little pieces, to crush her like a toad. With all his insight, hadn't Clovis seen yet? Hadn't he guessed anything?

He had seen and understood so well, Old Clovis had, that he was asking his friend to make the supreme sacrifice, for love of Crache-à-Pic. Maria was too much in view. When bootleggers began interfering in people's private lives, things stopped being private and turned to high drama. In this case Maria was the smuggler's card — that was crystal-clear.

"Even if you just pretend."

Just pretend! But did Clovis imagine for a single second that Ti-Louis — Ti-Louis-the-Lover — could ever have played the game for real? And besides, who was he, an orphan from the States, a twenty-year-old vagabond, to set himself up as Quicksilver's rival?

"And against Quicksilver, too!"

Old Clovis was on the point of saying, "Maria's not choosy . . . ," but checked the words just in time.

"Maria's at the age," he corrected himself, "where she'll be interested in the advances of a young blood like you. Thirty, thirty-five . . . it's the age when a woman will do the craziest things."

That was the saddest day in the whole of Ti-Louis's life. He set off for the dunes dragging his boots and leaving huge holes in the sand as if a giant had passed that way. Feet like lead.

. . . Maria! With her reddish mane, and her shifty eyes, and her large swaying hips, and her muffled laugh. . . . She's not straight, whatever that damned Old Clovis says. Of course it's not her fault, she hasn't been too lucky in life. But nobody on the coast has had much luck. They just have to make do. Was Crache-à-Pic any more spoiled by life? But Crache-à-Pic is something else. The world's never seen her like. And never will, that's for sure. Which means most men have to settle for a Maria. Because Crache-à-Pic is for Quicksilver or nobody. . . . If anything ever happened to that man, Crache-à-Pic would never want another, never. . . . Maria! What got into her to want to go and stick herself in between them? Nothing for it, have to get her out of there. With a pick-axe, or a rope, or anything at all, have to get her out of there.

And swelling his chest, planting his legs wide apart, and throwing his head back, Ti-Louis the Whistler coughed up a manly kind of laugh that fell as flat as a pancake on the sand.

"But, Holy Mother of Jesus Christ, how do you go about that anyway?"

. . . Any way at all, Ti-Louis, but not that way.

He lifted his head towards the weathercock, which was chuckling away with its beak pointed south-southwest.

. . . Get your harmonica out, Ti-Louis. And while you're at it, why not try the accordion? Old Cyprien left plenty of antiques in a chest in Célestine's attic. Why not take up the accordion to tickle the ears of the folk around here, and get them talking about you again?

"Why shouldn't I try the accordion, for a change?"

The late Cyprien's accordion drew quite a crowd to Clovis's forge, and Ti-Louis did get them talking about him again.

"That youngster's got a touch of the devil in him."

"He's got a music-box for a belly, that he has, by God!"

"That Ti-Louis could play you a tune on your ribs."

"Whoever shares his bed will go to sleep with notes running up and down her backbone every night."

This last comment reached the ears of Maria, as Clovis had intended it to. And Maria's ears tingled.

Clovis was right, the sailor's girl wasn't choosy. The more fish swam in her pond, the more she swam in it herself. As soon as she felt the musician's gaze caressing her forehead and cheeks, she became mad about his music.

Towards the middle of June Crache-à-Pic took Tobie with her and put out to sea. The *Sea-Cow* and Tobie, that was all she had left that was true, loyal, incorruptible.

"All right," she says between her teeth, "let them all go: the Twins, Jimmy, Céleste, Ti-Louis, and . . . yes, the whole bunch! Dieudonné will get them all in the end, one after another. To hell with them!"

Tobie comes over and sits beside her, looking out to sea.

"Where are we going?"

"To the end of the world."

"To Miscou . . . ?"

"No, Tobie, don't worry. We won't go past Cocagne Island."

Tobie calms down. She strokes his hair. . . . Don't worry. We'll start over. All alone this time, just us Crache-à-Pics. The others didn't measure up. They all backed off at the first little breeze. You could have expected that with Jimmy

— give him an inch and he takes a mile. Dieudonné must have offered him the joystick of his airplane. Céleste, well . . . she's his mother, she's not going to say anything against him. Ti-Louis, that's more surprising. I'd never have thought a girl . . . and Maria into the bargain! As for the Twins, well . . . Aglaé must be turning in her grave.

"No matter, Tobie. We're here, you and me. And nobody is going to be able to separate the last of the Crache-à-Pics, not even . . . nobody, Tobie."

. . . What's got into that Maria, the hussy! Shut up, Crache-à-Pic, you're starting to sound like Marie-Pet. Maria can do what she likes with her life. She's not the one to blame.

And Crache-à-Pic hauls in the sheet, yanks at the tiller, strains the sail, and runs the schooner so wild the *Sea-Cow* doesn't know which way to turn her prow.

"Hello!"

Crache-à-Pic comes to abruptly and lets the sails fall. It's him, Quicksilver, standing in his cutter.

"What's going on?"

He comes alongside. Tobie lets down the ladder. But Crache-à-Pic doesn't move; she stays there, back to the mast. Quicksilver jumps on deck and comes over.

"The *Sea-Cow* having trouble with her stays? She seemed to be swaying all over the place."

"Is that what attracts a constable, the way a thing sways?"

. . . !

They stare at each other the time of a gulp and a sigh. Then Quicksilver makes the first move, laughs and says,

"I think it's high time we had a serious talk, Crache-à-Pic."

"I think it's already too late."

"Come on, I've got things to say to you."

"Don't touch me, traitor."

Tobie comes over and instinctively slips between them. Crache-à-Pic puts her arm around his neck.

"Don't be afraid, Tobie, I won't let anyone hurt you. Nobody's going to come messing around in our lives ever again."

Quicksilver devours her with his eyes, his heart, his body. What a woman! What a splendid front she puts up. Then he in turn lifts his eyes to the heavens to implore the weathercock. At what angle should he approach her? On what tack? At what height? But she doesn't leave him time to find her weak point.

"If it's my schooner you want, prove your right of requisition. But first let Tobie and me go back to Cap-Lumière. And afterwards never set foot there again. Never."

She shows him the ladder. Quicksilver makes a move to take her in his arms, but at that instant Tobie stiffens in all his limbs and lets out a moan that begins to sound like a cry. Quicksilver's eyes widen in alarm. Crache-à-Pic quickly puts her arms around her brother, rocking him and murmuring endearments.

" . . . It's nothing, Tobie, it'll soon be over. . . . Shh. . . . It was just in fun. . . ."

Then, casting a look at Quicksilver that is at once angry and beseeching:

"It's epilepsy," she whispers above the head of her innocent brother.

The fit Crache-à-Pic feared doesn't materialize. Tobie calms down. But once the first danger is past, Quicksilver realizes he must leave.

"There'll be lots of time," he says to himself, "to explain things to her."

Time! . . . No one is master of time, Old Clovis the centenarian was to say to my father. Unless the weathercock intervenes.

And the weathercock did, once again, seizing in its beak the passing moment that had blundered between its wings. Several times before, the country had seen the weathercock put a stop to time like this, granting a short respite to life.

"And that's how it was," said Clovis, "that Quicksilver didn't put out to sea that night as he was supposed to."

It was a night of midsummer storm that prevented Dieudonné from bringing off the greatest coup in his life. And it kept the officer in port too. For the smuggler who had thought to draw the constable into his net by bringing him into the arms of his servant had in truth opened his barn door to a fox even slyer than himself. While stroking Maria's back, Quicksilver had loosened her tongue. One thing led to another, and the hired help helped him by opening all the locks and lifting all the trapdoors for him, even the one that hid the telegraph and its secret code of *dog, chair, bird, chicken, pigeon*. Quicksilver had a better memory than the Damien boy, and a better grasp of spelling than Télesphore. He learnt the code by heart, and once he was back home again, he set going an exchange of ultra-secret messages that told him the day, the hour, and the place of the rendezvous between big Dieudonné, Master of the Gulf, and the giant Al Capone, Master of All the Americas.

But for this one midsummer's eve the weathercock swirled, swerved, fell into a fit, and closed the sea to all adventurers. It was a night of dance for the whales and of orgy for the sharks. But as for men — be they Legs Diamond himself or the real McCoy or all Al Capone's gang put together — they couldn't leave port. Nor Dieudonné either.

And that's how Quicksilver got his night of reprieve.

He doesn't know how to tackle the short-tempered, stubborn, blustering Crache-à-Pic. So he decides to present her the evidence of the others first. . . . No, Crache-à-Pic, Jimmy-the-Flea didn't betray you. It's true he was pulled into Dieudonné's dream and was more or less attracted to it, but don't get things wrong. Jimmy is a wily little character who likes to flit round the fire, fascinated by the splendid colour of the flames, but he has the instinct to know just when to fold his wings. The proof is, it was Jimmy who slipped me one of my best tips, one he got from Black Willy.

"The little bugger!"

" . . . He slipped it to me without really noticing, to tell the truth."

"I know the drill. You got him to spill secrets he wouldn't even tell his mother."

"That's true. Which proves you were wrong to blame Céleste for being in on things. Céleste is totally outside all that. Her only fault is her cackling and her useless gossip. About Adalbert and Dagobert, for example. . . ."

Crache-à-Pic presses her lips together and hardens her forehead. And Quicksilver undertakes to defend the adoptive fathers of all Cap-Lumière.

. . . The poor Twins, even the two of them together had never been able to assemble enough words to fashion a coherent speech. Not even that day of the great aborted question, when the two suitors kneeling at Aglaé's feet hadn't been able to muster more than an evening of sighs, sighs which were to stretch out over the next twenty years.

Crache-à-Pic can't help smiling at this evocation of one of the dearest and funniest memories of her childhood. But she checks herself immediately, determined not to pardon the guilty pair so easily.

. . . They would find words to defend a Crache-à-Pic if necessary, Quicksilver continues, but not to justify themselves. It should be added that the tunnel Black Willy dragged them into proved to be pretty tortuous. And the twins hadn't completely extricated themselves yet.

"That tunnel wasn't just a hideout, it was the general headquarters of the bootleggers. And in the exact middle of it, our Twins, down on all fours, took Black Willy by the throat and made him cough up everything, beginning with Jimmy-the-Flea. That Adal-Gobert is a two-headed eel if ever there was one!"

And Crache-à-Pic's laughter blends with Quicksilver's.

"So you see, none of your men was ever unfaithful to you."

"Oh no? Not even Ti-Louis the Whistler?"

And she pulls the pretty pout of a woman deceived:

"I would have thought that he at least. . . ."

But Quicksilver doesn't let her continue. He gently places two fingers on her lips, and envelops her in a smile so tender and captivating that she feels the marrow melt in the hollow of her bones. . . . Ti-Louis the Whistler, Crache-à-Pic, remains the most pure, the most loyal, the most knightly of hidden suitors. Don't be fooled by his youth and guileless candour. And don't go thinking. . . .

"No, Crache-à-Pic, the Whistler didn't deceive you. The orphan from the States found a country and a family here. And besides, he's become a man now."

"In the arms of that . . . that whore!" she snaps.

. . . The jealous woman, thinks Quicksilver. Not jealous of Ti-Louis but of Maria — and behind Maria, it's the constable she's aiming at. She's leading him straight to the ultimate showdown, while the others stand like guardian angels around the gates of their paradise. But Quicksilver respects these angels and knows Crache-à-Pic's attachment to her crew. He wants to restore them to her cleansed of every suspicion his presence has raised.

"Maria's a bit loose, perhaps. The poor girl can't help it, she was born flesh and blood. But your Ti-Louis the Whistler is as much a skirt-chaser as I am a choirboy. . . ."

She cuts in:

"What difference do you think that makes to me? Ti-Louis is free, Maria's free . . . they've all left their mother's apron strings, they're free to drag around wherever they want . . . in the swamps, the woods, the dunes, the barns. . . . "

He seizes her again and puts his hand over her mouth, but she jerks free.

"That's right, you're a choirboy!" she shouts. "Anyone who thinks he can step into the middle of the forge and brag that he can have Crache-à-Pic is a choirboy."

Quicksilver measures the breadth and depth of her scorn. This woman is even prouder than he thought. Love hasn't quenched or softened her fiery spirit, it's given it wings! And how — without breaking them — can he keep her from flying away?

"Maybe I should tell you something about my secret relations with Maria. . . . "

"You couldn't tell me anything I don't know already."

"But if I explained what I was doing with her in the barn. . . ."

"I'd plug my ears!"

"How can I make you understand that I'm a constable, a representative of the law. . . ."

"Don't give yourself the trouble, I've known that from the start."

" . . . make you understand that for an officer a woman can be used as bait. . . ."

. . . !

Damn! Too late. He won't even attempt to take it back. It's no time to be arguing like a Jesuit anyway! He gets up, stands tall beside her, peers towards shore.

"Look," he says to Crache-à-Pic, pointing towards the apple tree in her back yard. "I'll bet there's a carpet of apple blossom there, softer than marsh grass or dune brambles."

She follows his arm stretched towards her home, then suddenly:

"Where's the bear?" she says.

"Tobie took him to the woods early this afternoon. I saw them going off like a couple of pals."

"And you sent them, to get them out of the way!"

"I didn't speak to either Tobie or the bear, on my word of honour as an officer."

"And on the head of a Crache-à-Pic, who did you speak to?"

"For some time now, someone's been teaching me to speak to the weathercock."

Crache-à-Pic's breath is cut short. This man is a star fallen from the firmament. Never, here at home or at the ends of the earth, has she met a being who could put his feet in her tracks like that. Why, oh why, does he have to be on the side of the law?

He sees her struggling between love and honour, between him and her ancestors buried there beneath the apple tree, and he risks everything.

"Crache-à-Pic, trust me, just this once. I'll never ask you again. But this one time, follow me to the sacred tree of your family — and I will swear there, to the shade of your own grandfather, that I have never loved any other woman, that I never will love any other; you yourself will be my witness."

She trembles. Yet she dredges up one last swagger.

"You know my dead ancestors will take a terrible revenge on anyone who doesn't tell the truth."

"I know what I risk. I've known it since the first time I set foot under that damned apple tree."

And before she can even open her mouth, he picks her up and carries her off, striding across the dunes in his seven-league boots.

Before the sun disappears at the top of the field, Crache-à-Pic has just the time to extract one last promise from Quicksilver:

"Tomorrow morning you'll give me Dieudonné's new code."

And the sun went down to the sounds of *dog, chair, pigeon, toad, chicken* . . . coming from the bootleggers' barn, and echoed from the Crache-à-Pics' apple tree where the new Adam and Eve slept on dried flowers of paradise.

Next day Quicksilver regretted having turned Dieudonné's code over to Crache-à-Pic. Drunk with the splendours of a night perfumed by apple blossom, he had not been able to refuse the one favour she had asked in exchange for hers.

"She's so fearless — if I know her, she just may venture out to sea tonight and try to slip into the middle of things."

He knew her, all right — completely fearless — for this was exactly the plan she had been brewing since dawn, by the light of the morning star.

The north wind had died down. The eve of La Saint-Jean promised to be favourable for bootlegging. Everyone would be out at sea, thought Quicksilver, and Crache-à-Pic would not be able to resist being there at the rendezvous. Just to thumb her nose graciously at the others from the deck of her *Sea-Cow*. There was no use pleading with her, warning her of the danger, putting her on her guard against Al Capone's men who'd stop at nothing; it would be a waste of time. The very name of Al Capone would only be an added temptation.

He paced heavily over the sand, to the great surprise of Old Ozite, who couldn't see the wings on his heels that day. For the first time the constable seemed preoccupied and worried. Then suddenly Ozite saw him stop at the stern of the *Sea-Cow* and sniff it. . . . She had a sharp eye, the old centenarian did, to be able to see a man sniff at more than five hundred feet! But Ozite never took back a word she'd spoken before witnesses; she stuck to her story that, on the eve of La Saint-Jean, Quicksilver had spent part of the afternoon sniffing the *Sea-Cow*.

Well, let that pass.

Towards evening he happened upon Ti-Louis the Whistler, by chance or design. And the two men had a long conversation. Then, Ozite declared, she lost sight of them.

It was almost night when Crache-à-Pic came down to the dock and discovered the crime: her *Sea-Cow* had disappeared. Oh no! Not that! She had learnt to play the big game: if you agree to lie with the lousy fox, you have to expect to scratch. But not this! She'd take on anyone herself, but let those who touched her dear ones beware. And the *Sea-Cow* was her child, her creation, the artist's masterpiece. The schooner was practically born from her own hands, certainly from her soul. And without considering the significance of her act, she raised her arms to the heavens and called down the wrath of all her ancestors.

... The Crache-à-Pics were a stiff-necked race, Old Clovis concluded. Living or dead, they had spines stiffer than schooners' mainmasts.

Quicksilver was already far out over the horizon when Crache-à-Pic's curse echoed in the ancestral tomb at the foot of the apple tree. If the unlucky woman had known who had borrowed her schooner that night, she wouldn't have been so quick to invoke the dead to come to her aid. But she didn't find out who it was until the depths of the night — in Clovis's forge, to be precise. Ti-Louis had judged it wise to slip a word to his friend before he and Quicksilver embarked for this mysterious rendezvous. Just in case.

Old Clovis said later that, when she wormed the secret out of him, Crache-à-Pic at first seemed relieved.

"She split her sides laughing, but with a laugh that seemed a mite tattered, as if she had stones in her spleen. Then she said, 'At least I'll get even with Dieudonné.' "

Out there on the sea, Quicksilver and Ti-Louis were making the most of the starlight and were delving the celestial genealogy of Sainte-Marie-des-Côtes.

The Great Bear — Crache-à-Pic
The Little Bear — Tobie
The Lyre — Ti-Louis the Whistler
Gemini — Adalbert-Dagobert
Orion — The Three Kings
The Pleiades — The network of cousins and sisters-in-law

Pegasus — Clovis the storyteller
The Serpent — Marie-Pet
The Milky Way — Sainte-Marie-des-Côtes and its thirty-six
hamlets. . . .
Suddenly Quicksilver catches Ti-Louis by the arm.

"And Hydra, the monster with nine heads, . . . " he says, "there he is, reflected in the water off to starboard. Don't move, mate."

Ti-Louis doesn't. Quicksilver, his idol, is also his captain tonight. The mate will obey.

Quicksilver takes down Crache-à-Pic's sou'wester, which is hanging in the rigging, puts it on, and pulls it down over his eyes.

"Go down below, Ti-Louis, and wait till I call. I'll whistle three times, like this."

And Quicksilver puts his fingers to his lips and imitates the cry of a young gull in spring.

"Is it the *Kouchibougouac*?" asks Ti-Louis, just to hear the sound of his own voice.

"For the time being it's just Dieudonné. Soon we'll see the *Dragon* show up. Al Capone's men keep their finger on the trigger all the time. No sense provoking them. Stay down below. Don't come up on deck till I signal. Swear you won't."

"I swear," says Ti-Louis, making the sign of the cross on mouth, throat, and chest.

"Hurry up now, lad. . . . At sunrise you can play me a brand new tune on your harmonica."

And in an exchange of smiles that made the Virgin blush and old Betelgeuse wink, the two Knights of the Starry Sky went each to his post, without a word or wave of farewell.

It's Black Willy who spots the schooner first.

"The *Cow*!" he shouts.

Dieudonné hurries up on deck.

"What!"

That she-demon! Her again. . . . Well, guess what, my little vixen, this time you're going to get it! There are limits to a man's patience. And tonight the limits are right here, between the dunes and the stars and the open sea.

"But how did she get to know the time and place, the slut? For once we. . . . You been talking to your wife, Joe?"

Joe Colossus makes a schoolboy face. Dieudonné should know well enough that while he was rotting in prison in the States his wife. . . .

"Never mind!" says Dieudonné, grinding his teeth. "Right now we've got to get her out of our hair before the *Dragon* turns up. I'm going to send her a warning that'll make her sit up and take notice for the rest of the night, the bitch."

And he dives into the cabin.

Joe Colossus and Black Willy look worried when they see their chief reappear with the rifle. But Dieudonné pushes them aside and rests his elbows on the rail. He aims for the mast, but at the last minute fires into the air.

The schooner doesn't flinch. She is now within hailing distance. Dieudonné keeps her in his sights and yells,

"That's enough, Crache-à-Pic! I'm warning you! You've got ten seconds to bring that damned carcass around and head back to Cap-Lumière. I'm counting."

Silence. Nothing moves. And the night has no witness of the two ships with their threatening prows, other than the stars above.

Suddenly the schooner stirs. Dieudonné thinks she's

drawing away. Then he steps back instinctively on seeing this wreck, handled by a single woman, bearing straight down on him . . . the prow reaches up, fines down, cuts the waves like a knife.

Stop!

. . . At the sound of the shot, the sky throws down a thousand shooting stars that splash into the sea. Then sea and sky are dumb, for an eternity.

Black Willy is the first to stir; he seizes the rifle from his chief's hands and throws it overboard. Then he speaks:

"The cursed witch asked for it. From now on. . . ."

But Dieudonné raises his arm, and Black Willy leaves his sentence unfinished. He understands that he must go aboard, to see.

The two hulls are touching. Black Willy can jump across. The sea is now so slick that the motionless *Sea-Cow* seems sculpted in glass.

Time drags on and on . . . to the point where, for the first time in his life, Dieudonné thinks it has stopped. His shirt collar is choking him; he runs two fingers around it only to discover that he's not wearing a shirt, just a woollen sweater. What's Black Willy doing?

He's not doing a thing. He's standing there, arms dangling, stunned. Mute and frozen stiff. So Dieudonné dredges up a sound from his own throat:

"Did I get her . . . ?"

And from the deck of the *Sea-Cow* he hears a choked cry:

"Dieudonné, you've killed Quicksilver."

The cry has pierced Ti-Louis the Whistler's eardrums, it reverberates through his skull. Dieudonné, you've killed Quicksilver! Dieudonné, you've killed Quicksilver! The bulk-

266

heads echo, vibrate, lurch, making him reel. He swore to obey Quicksilver, not to come up on deck before the signal. The signal has come — but from the depths of hell!

Now you're released from your oath, Ti-Louis. You can go up into the night. You can go up on deck and take them by the throat, the monsters, and make them spit blood. You can . . . but he can't do a thing, he can't move his legs, his whole body is welded to the floor of the hold.

So it's his body that feels the first blow of the axe. Someone's chopping overhead. The *Sea-Cow* moans and trembles, but resists. What are they doing to her? Another blow, and another . . . the mast! They're chopping down the mast! Ti-Louis springs up like a stag. He's found his legs again. He bounds up, climbs the ladder, sticks his head through the hatch, and lifts his gaze to the mainmast at the very instant the timber cracks and falls, the mainsail encasing it like a shroud. Ti-Louis turns and sees the silhouette of a giant stepping over the gunwale and jumping aboard the *Kouchibougouac*.

An engine backfires. Then nothing.

Out there in the distance, while Joe Colossus takes the wheel and steers for the first point of Sainte-Marie-des-Côtes, Black Willy is trying to find words strong and convincing enough to reassure his master.

. . . The abandoned schooner will float around for a day or two before some fisherman runs across her. Meantime she'll have crossed the path of the *Dragon* several times, for it can't be far away. And Al Capone's shoulders are plenty broad enough to carry one more . . . uh . . . accident, so you don't have to lose any sleep over Al Capone.

When the three poachers came upon Crache-à-Pic's schooner floating like a barge, without sails or mast, they were dumbfounded. If they had been able to speak, no doubt they would have found their presence as Three Kings out of place; this scene resembled a Pietà more than a Nativity.

At the foot of the broken mast sat Ti-Louis the Whistler, with Quicksilver's head in his lap, and as he drew the sounds of a funeral dirge from his harmonica, pearls of sea spray ran down his cheeks.

In one movement, the Three Kings removed their caps and knelt.

And once again it was Old Clovis pushing his wheelbarrow who was first to see the floating funeral procession: his friends the poachers' fishing boat towing a decapitated *Sea-Cow*, in total silence, under the morning sun.

Soon the whole village was alerted.

"Go get the doctor!"

"It's too late. Better tell the priest."

"It's even too late for the priest."

"I'd say it's the justice of the peace we want, and a magistrate. He's got a bullet through his forehead."

"Don't you think we should tell Crache-à-Pic? . . . It's her schooner."

"It's her schooner," all Sainte-Marie-des-Côtes murmured in chorus.

Then a woman's voice rose timidly from the crowd.

"And it was her man."

The crowd never had time to echo the words. They fell back, stupidly, to let Crache-à-Pic pass through holding her brother Tobie by the hand. The two of them climbed on board the schooner, approached the scene, and hung their heads in silence. Then Crache-à-Pic lifted a corner of the sail and covered Quicksilver's body. And it was only then that she shivered all over and began to tremble in every limb. Her head raised to the heavens, she let a sob rise in her throat so long and so profound that in that instant all Sainte-Marie-des-Côtes felt a stab in the pit of their stomachs.

"After that," Clovis predicted, "the coast will never again let it be said that Crache-à-Pic was no woman."

And as if this woman had heard Old Clovis's prophecy, she straightened up, stared out over Sainte-Marie-des-Côtes to Dieudonné's domain, and shouted,

"The dead will avenge the dead!"

A silence like lead descended over the whole country.

But at the very moment that Crache-à-Pic opened her mouth to continue her malediction, the crowd turned suddenly towards poor Tobie and a murmur ran from mouth to mouth:

. . . Epilepsy . . . the boy's having a fit . . . watch out for Tobie. . . .

Crache-à-Pic has just heard. She turns and sees her epileptic brother twisting like a worm and beginning to drool. She cries out, "Tobie!", pushes aside Céleste, Célestine, and the other women, and takes her brother in her arms. She opens his mouth to free his tongue, rubs his temples, holds him with all her strength, and rocks him back and forth. Clovis, who has drawn near, hears her almost singing:

. . . Hush, Tobie . . . don't cry . . . he'll come back, Quicksilver will. . . . They were afraid of him because he was the strongest, the biggest, the handsomest . . . but he'll come back, like Grandfather Crache-à-Pic, and he'll strike like thunder and dash the mast of their ship and the shell of their barn into the sea . . . you'll see. . . . Don't worry, Tobie,

I'm here, I'll stay with you. . . . Because they'll never . . . never get the better of the Crache-à-Pics!

Then she lets her head fall to the neck of her trembling brother and weeps silently.

Sainte-Marie-des-Côtes hears no sound but the heart-rending strains of the harmonica, and the tinkling bell of the altar boy preceding the priest through the dune hay.

CHAPTER SIX

LA SAINT-JEAN, 1933.

Céleste climbs on a chair in the Crache-à-Pics' kitchen, moves the hands to twelve, and stills the pendulum. He must have died about midnight. Then she climbs down backwards and steps on the tail of the cat, who lets out an ear-splitting howl.

Crache-à-Pic turns from the window to see where the silence is coming from. Then she notices the clock: noon . . . midnight . . . noon. . . . Time is transfixed there, over her head. She goes back to her window.

. . . It's not enough to stop the pendulum, Céleste. Go tell the weathercock. Make him stop, once and for all. The south-west winds will never blow over this country again. The weathercock can do what he likes — squirm, twist, spin like crazy — he can never bring back those hot, caressing winds to the coast. You can flap your wings till they jump their joints, moan and whine to the creator of heaven and earth, you'll never rewind the skein of time. It stopped, swallowing up both past and future, on the eve of the Feast of Saint Jean.

My father was told the rest of this story in one sitting, start to finish. But this time, as Old Clovis himself admitted, his view of the world was taken from the other eye, and from a little higher up. For during that whole summer of

271

1933 Clovis occupied the front row of the jury box at Dieudonné's trial.

Oh yes, Dieudonné came to trial all right. Had to. All the evidence pointed to him. He had put out to sea on the eve of La Saint-Jean, he admitted it — accompanied by Black Willy and Joe Colossus and no one else. That was true. That could be proved. The Damien boys had spent the night at their father's rebuilding his barn, ten men on the work gang were witness to that. As for the poachers from Grand-Digue, they were obliged to admit they'd been caught red-handed that night, but nowhere near the rendezvous with Al Capone. It was the first time two fishermen were ever so eager to spread around that they'd been caught poaching undersized lobsters. But after all, in a trial for the murder of an officer of the law it's a lucky man who has even the slightest alibi ready. . . . I took two hundred pounds in six traps, the poacher proclaimed; the judge himself was obliged to remind him that he was under oath and mustn't exaggerate. And all the other bootleggers in Dieudonné's pay could provide alibis too.

No, that night the *Kouchibougouac* had carried only three men to the rendezvous with the big racketeers. There was Black Willy and Joe Colossus. And Dieudonné, of course.

The judge had an English name . . . Urk-something-or-other . . . , came from the south of the province, and addressed the court in his own tongue. He had brought his interpreter along with him, which meant everybody heard the same story twice over. So when daughter-in-law Jeannette had the nerve to claim she'd never said such-and-such . . . well, she'd said it in French and in English, and an old chin-wagger's ear doesn't deceive him. And anyway, it's all written down.

The clerk of the court, as they call him, took it all down word for word. Jeannette's prattle along with all the rest. And Marie-Pet's and Long-Tongue Médard's too.

It was Médard who was called to the stand first. Not that he'd seen much, the blabbermouth, but as usual he talked louder than everybody else put together, which made him seem better informed. Informed! . . . Phffft! . . . In the court clerk's place I wouldn't have gone raising calluses on my fingers taking down testimony like that. He saw the *Sea-Cow* come in to port early that morning with her mast broken, towed by a fishing boat. And he was the one who alerted the village, I grant you that, but it wasn't the first time; Long-Tongue Médard had been waking up the whole countryside every morning for the past thirty years. Which means that in my opinion the words of a bull-horn like that aren't worth the ink of your pen or the spit of my palate. But let that pass.

As for Marie-Pet, that was another kettle of fish. Not because of Dieudonné, or because of Quicksilver. Because of Crache-à-Pic. Marie-Pet had been waiting all her life for a chance like this. A platform all to herself, just think of it, in the presence of a judge, a court clerk, lawyers, the sheriff, uniformed guards, the whole apparatus of the law. Plus the curious, come from all four corners of the county. At last the old gossip was going to be able to give everyone a piece of her mind. She grabbed the bar with both hands.

For three hours she testified. She testified against slack morals that poisoned the very air she breathed, against the economic crisis that had already eaten up half her future . . .

". . . not that I've had the time to put much aside, don't go mistaking what I say . . . "

. . . against governments for letting things take their course, against the Church for not stopping them, against life for not being what it was in the good old days . . . against neighbours, relations, enemies, rivals, competitors, opponents, against you and against me, and against Crache-à-Pic.

. . . Crache-à-Pic!

. . . Yes indeed! A man is dead. I saw his corpse, I can swear to that. But whose fault was it? Who was it pushed him into going to sea that night? And the proof is, he didn't die on his own ship, poor man, may God rest his soul! He was killed on the deck of a schooner that wasn't even his. And what was this schooner doing out at sea in the middle of the night, I'd like to know? And how come the captain of this ship wasn't on board as a captain should be? Makes you think, doesn't it? It's been a long while now that certain persons I wouldn't like to name . . . for I didn't come before the judge to accuse anybody, despite the fact that I've seen things coming for a long time now. . . . Yes, anybody with a speck of judgement could have predicted the sorry events that took place on that tragic and unfortunate night. . . .

Ooof! She was taking herself for a regular schoolmarm. . . .

. . . So don't come around afterwards asking me. . . .

Nobody was asking her anything. She could save her breath to cool her porridge. Indeed, the tribunal might have asked her to shut up if a single lawyer, or the judge himself, had been able to get a word in edgewise. But she had the bit in her teeth. She shook the bar with all her might, as if she were in the box at the Last Judgement and the salvation of the world depended on the case she was pleading. Then she turned towards the jury and looked us straight in the eye. Even the jurors from l'Anse-aux-Outardes who didn't know her so well were kind of impressed. She began to attack us all in person — us, the delegates of the law, responsible for morality and public welfare; us, the chosen twelve named by the tribunal — accusing us of slack morals, treachery, and disrespect for life. She laid a man's death on our shoulders.

. . . It all begins by neglecting your evening prayers at the foot of your bed; then you give up the mass and the sacraments. That's what a life of sin leads to. Don't ask me, after that, why a crime's been committed on this coast. . . .

While the witness was catching her breath, the defence managed to indicate to her that she wasn't being asked to identify the cause of the crime, but to shed light on the circumstances surrounding the death. The defence was wrong to ask her anything whatsoever. Asking Marie-Pet to shed light on the circumstances was like asking the Pope to speak Latin. She rode her deposition like a flying carpet. The judge finally had to step in himself — when he saw us wiping our foreheads one after another, and coughing and clearing our throats fit to spit blood into our handkerchiefs. So His Honour let out with three cracks of his hammer — that little mallet on the top of his desk — and. . . . That's enough, Madame Caissie! Next!

And all that in both languages.

If His Honour had known who was coming up next, nose in the air, head high, clutching her evidence under her arm (all written down beforehand on a piece of flowery paper), he'd have skipped that witness and gone straight on to Melchior or Xavier-the-Hunchback. But he would have to pass daughter-in-law Jeannette first, because she knew the accused better than anyone, according to her say-so, on account of having played dominoes with his wife of a winter evening. Therefore she could attest to the amiability and distinguished manners of a man . . .

" . . . too worthy and generous and well bred to have the soul of an assassin, Your Honour."

Ah! There you're laying it on too thick, daughter-in-law. Always clean, she says, and well dressed. Who wouldn't dress up in silks and furs if he had the means to buy his glad rags at the T. Eaton Company? . . . He doesn't chase other men's wives or get drunk on Saturday nights like just about every other man on the coast, Your Honour. But go on and tell the judge who it is supplies the Saturday-night drunkards with their rum, Jeannette! Maybe other men's wives might have something to complain to the court about along that line. . . . Oh! Now listen to her! Dieudonné's a just, decent man who never robbed anybody! If I ever get out of this jury box I'll just-and-decent-man you! I'll put a few new twists in that little bun on your head, see if I don't. Just and decent, my foot! Just look at the folk from the coast counting the knots in their benches while you read out your speech about the just and decent man. These folk who didn't play dominoes with his wife last winter aren't about to believe in your fine Dieudonné's justice! Nor will anybody who bought his gramophones on credit either. Nor anybody who sold him their lands for nothing. . . . He doesn't spit, she says. I reckon not. It's pipe tobacco makes a man spit, not big cigars from the tropics.

"He don't spit in the spittoon, that one, he spits in our faces."

"Hee-hee-hee!"

"Silence!"

"Order in the court! *Ordre dans la cour!*"

Well now! The court clerk's turned bilingual too.

Things are warming up. The defence sees there's nothing more to be got out of the daughter-in-law. The big gawk trails down the main aisle, her dress spread out like a peacock tail behind her. From his box Dieudonné smiles at his wife, who thanks Jeannette with a nod of her head. All is not lost. There'll be more dominoes yet.

When the Twins were called, Dieudonné must have been thinking of that little spin over the woods in the airplane looking for Tobie. Good investment, that. And he looked at them both with fellow-feeling and doggy eyes. But Adalbert and Dagobert — blinded by the lights of the courtroom, deafened by the murmur of the crowd whispering their names, and choking on their own saliva — responded to neither the accused's look, nor the prosecutor's. In fact the Twins were responding to nobody, not even the judge and the lawyers. Even the court clerk had to start over three times to make them swear to tell the truth, the whole truth, and nothing but the truth, so help them God. Each Twin placed his hand over his brother's hand on top of the Bible and replied at the same time when either name was called.

Moreover, when the interpreter undertook to translate for the benefit of the judge, the only unilingual member of the court . . . yes indeed, everyone on the coast spoke two languages even in those days, two half-languages, two something-or-others that passed for languages, some even spoke both at the same time . . . when the interpreter tried to translate the names Adalbert and Dagobert, such a gurgle came out of his throat the judge raised his eyebrows to the heavens, lowered them again, cupped his left hand to his ear, screwed his mouth into the shape of a conch shell and. . . .

"Bhrrrt?" he said.

The whole courtroom thought His Honour was having digestive problems.

This wasn't the end of the poor judge's troubles with the Twins. After their names had been stated, their identities had to be sorted out. For according to the most reliable authorities in the country, after fifty years of fusion the Twins themselves weren't ready to swear on the Bible as to exactly who was who. And what was the harm in that? Each felt so much at home in the other's skin that neither aspired to autonomy.

If the Twins aspired to anything during Dieudonné's trial, it was to get this ritual over as soon as possible so they could quietly go back home. The fishing season would soon be starting, and this year Adal-Gobert were responsible for feeding the whole of Cap-Lumière. Neither Crache-à-Pic nor Céleste had the heart to put out nets or dredge the slime of the bay for clams. The Twins didn't have any time to waste in court, and for that matter they felt about as much at ease there as a bee in a spiderweb. So they resolved to get out fast, come hell or high water.

Old Clovis's Adam's apple danced a jig at the memory of that spiderweb; in the end the judge, the lawyers, the interpreter, and the clerk were all caught up in its toils, like no other county court in history . . . while Adalbert and Dagobert scurried out of the courtroom and headed back to Cap-Lumière without a glance at anyone.

. . . Not a glance, not even at me, Clovis, for fear they'd burst out laughing. The judge should have taken things in hand. To keep track of who was who, he should have separated them by simply putting one on the right of the accused and the other on the left. But by the time the Crown got this idea the Twins had already seen it coming, and spent their time passing back and forth from left to right, and contradicting themselves by yessing each other's nos and vice versa, and by repeating each other's statement backwards, then setting it right way round again a minute later. His Honour did try at one point to accuse one Twin of contradicting himself and therefore of false testimony, but the other immediately stepped forward to declare that *he* was the one who'd said that, he'd swear on the gospel.

When the Twins finally left the courtroom at the end of July, the judge and the two lawyers sent out — even though it was right in the middle of Prohibition — for a big glass of *whisky blanc* each.

"Hand on the Bible."

She put her hand on the Bible.

"Your right hand."

"I'm left-handed."

The court clerk raised an eye to the interpreter who mumbled a couple of words to the judge who shrugged his shoulders and replied "Okay" in English.

"Okay," repeated the interpreter, and then the court clerk.

In both languages.

So Maria swore to tell the truth, the whole truth, and nothing but the truth, lefthandedly.

Yet the testimony that bore the closest resemblance to the truth, according to Old Clovis, came from the heart of this girl who had got the handsome Quicksilver under her skin and couldn't find it in herself to pardon fate.

. . . Dieudonné had hired her as a servant, supposedly to help Zéphirine . . . can you mend and polish? he had asked.

What a question! What girl of thirty on the coast doesn't know how to mend! She had accepted the offer. It was a pittance, but she got her meals. At home she had a mother and a kid to look after, and a child-mother hasn't got fifty-six choices, not everybody is ready to take her on, even at the lowest rate. Dieudonné knew all that better than anyone. He was the one who fixed the prices for the whole country. Once she got into the kitchen, it was clear to Maria that she wasn't needed, that Zéphirine wasn't expecting her, and that Dieudonné had other plans for her.

The court squirms, the interpreter hunts for words, the judge leans forward to hear better. And Annie from the presbytery makes the sign of the cross right down to her bellybutton.

"Order in the court!"

What he was asking of Maria, the scoundrel. . . .

"Say 'the accused'."

The accused, my ass.

Ohhh!

"He wanted my ass."

Sshhh! Silence! Order in the court!

But not for himself, for Quicksilver.

Dieudonné's wife hunches back in her seat and closes her eyes.

He had to get something on Quicksilver. . . .

"Refrain from identifying people by their nicknames."

"The deceased."

"His correct name was Mathieu-Martin Vigneault."

The audience comments on this for several minutes: So he wasn't a Martin but a Vigneault. . . . Related to the Vigneaults from Iles-de-la-Madeleine, do you think? There's still some of the family in the south of the province. . . .

Most of them left the region at the time of the Great Disruption.... It must be that branch, he must be descended from our own ancestors....

"Silence! Order in the court!"

It is only by threatening to clear the courtroom that the judge restores order. Mlle Allain may continue her testimony. Everyone looks around for Mlle Allain, including Maria, who finally catches on, draws breath, and continues. But her heart isn't in it any longer.

Yet she had come to court that morning determined to tell the judge everything: Dieudonné's secret scheming, his intrigues, his lies, his cunning, his wickedness. Jeannette could go take a jump at herself; the man wasn't decent. Manners, sure — even distinction. But woe to the person who stood in his way! And one night Quicksilver had found himself in Dieudonné's way.

At the memory of Quicksilver, dead at sea without a farewell for anyone, hard-bitten Maria, the pariah of the parish, let out a sob that softened the hearts of all Sainte-Marie-des-Côtes.

"It's too bad," she said, "that it has to be the good ones who lose every time."

And turning towards the jury:

"In your place, I wouldn't let such things happen."

The end of Maria's testimony left a hole in the low, continuous murmur of the courtroom. The flies took advantage of this, leaving the windowpanes to attack the judge's wig, while he defended himself with his mallet. Which is why Xavier-the-Hunchback's swearing-in was greeted by a huge blow on the desk that sent the dossier flying and the clerk scrambling on all fours to recover it. This little incident allowed the witness, leaning over the scattered papers, to only half-straighten up and to exaggerate his hump by a good foot. When the Crown wanted to interrogate him, the hunchback's answers didn't rise much higher than the nails in the floorboards. After five minutes the judge took pity on his interpreter, who was practically on his knees under the witness's hanging head. As he left the court Xavier-the-Hunchback straightened up and winked in the direction of the jury. As a witness he had got off with three phrases that nobody heard.

And the court clerk tore up his empty page.

Next came the cousins-and-sisters-in-law connection: Céleste, Célestine, Zéphirine. They tried to insist on appearing together, but were only allowed to follow each other in the witness box . . . which they did so closely that the sense of their evidence was unbroken, spun out from one mouth to the next. For instance, each of Céleste's statements ended with: " . . . which I have from my cousin Célestine," who was summarily called upon to corroborate this testimony but preferred to refer it to her sister-in-law Zéphirine "who I got this from," who was automatically called to the stand. But rather than confirm or deny, Zéphirine claimed she had it all from Céleste, her sister-in-law's cousin, who came back to the stand to pick up the thread of the story where she had left it, which meant to say at the preamble.

This time the tribunal lost patience. It was all very well to wear a wig and sit on the King's Bench and be descended from the first litter of Loyalists — a man's patience does have its limits. That day the limit was reached with Zéphirine, Célestine, and Céleste following each other into the witness box at the pace of a square dance, to the beat of the crowd keeping time by clapping their hands and stamping their feet.

Old Clovis himself admitted later that the trio of sister-in-law-cousins had well deserved the judge's reprimand when he referred to the coast as a country of undisciplined, inattentive, unreasonable, mindless scatterbrains. In English this was even more impressive, and several mothers unleashed a shower of smacks on their fidgety offspring.

But everything returned to normal with the arrival of a witness nobody was expecting. It was the Crown's surprise: ex-constable Martial.

. . . Ah! That was a fine surprise, all right. Everyone had the fondest memories of the officer, almost tender. They didn't hold it against him that he was less shrewd, less fast, less — let's come right out and say it — less quicksilver than some, or that he came from Pré-d'en-Haut. His entrance into the courtroom drew an ahhh! from the very walls and benches, no lie, and this gave the judge a better opinion of the country. At least these people show respect for the representatives of the law, he must have said to himself. . . . As far as that goes, the judge was right. Once he was gone, a man like Martial was respected and venerated by everybody.

So Martial took his place on the witness stand.

. . . The truth, the whole truth, and nothing but the truth. . . . Imagine! A constable! Imagine a constable giving false evidence! Although from what Ozite says . . . but you can't trust Old Ozite. Martial was sworn in, right hand on the Bible, swearing straight to the judge's face that what he had to say, he'd say, and that he hoped his revelations . . . that was his word . . . would help bring justice to the innocent and restore peace and order to society. He said all that, just like a schoolmaster in charge of the top grade.

It was the Crown that had called this important witness, dragging him away from his cushy retirement in the depths of the head office in the capital. A constable who had followed the comings and goings of the smugglers on land and sea for eight years . . . the court was surely going to hear some juicy tidbits! . . . Go ahead, Martial, it's your turn, remember the ghosts in Lovers' Lane, and the watch-ox tethered right over a smugglers' hideout, and the healthy invalids carried around in ambulances and even hearses. Remember the eight nights they stole from you right in the middle of winter . . . hee-hee! . . . remember? The banker's daughter had been threatened, her father had received a letter warning that his daughter was in danger, the constable had to step in and keep watch eight nights running . . . during which time the rum-runners were tearing around in sleighs filled right up to the brim and covered over in buffalo robes . . . ho-ho-ho! Remember, Martial?

. . . No, Martial didn't remember any of it. On the subject of bootleggers the constable remained mute. Here he was talking about the victim, the deceased Mathieu-Martin Vigneault, whom he used to know, or had heard about . . . an exceptional man, this new constable, unlike anyone else, a convert in a manner of speaking. That explained why this Quicksilver was so keen and passionate, why he gave himself to the job body and soul. He had a score to settle with life, with the world. . . . Martial didn't say with the smugglers, but the judge understood — everybody understood.

The person who must have understood first was the lawyer for the defence, because he took his turn interrogating Martial and pumped him for hours. . . . So that was it, eh? The victim had a score to settle with the bootleggers? Maybe with Dieudonné himself? And why was that, now? And since when? And what if it had been him attacking Dieudonné out there on the high seas, unbeknownst to everyone? . . .

Maybe this Vigneault wasn't an innocent victim after all, maybe there had been provocation. . . .

Benches squeak, buttocks squirm, heads turn, eyes shift. Someone's attacking Quicksilver? . . . That's not fair, this trial is going to end badly. . . . But Martial collects himself. He didn't mean to say that, he never accused the victim . . . he repeats that Mathieu-Martin Vigneault was a fine man, just and incorruptible, and that if he joined the ranks of the law it was to combat wrongdoers, all wrongdoers, including boot-leggers.

The defence stops him with a snap of the fingers:

"Bootleggers in particular?"

"Bootleggers like the rest."

"And why bootleggers?"

"He had his reasons."

"His reasons?"

. . . .

"Your Honour, I demand a reply. The witness is under oath."

The judge consults the interpreter, stares at the con-stable, and nods his wig in the direction of the defence.

Martial grasps the rail of the box with both hands, looks Dieudonné's lawyer in the eye, and says slowly,

"They did his father in ten years ago."

The flies can resume their buzzing and leave the windowpanes again. The courtroom is breathless. The defence lawyer returns to his bench, arms dangling. Dieu-donné, who was smiling at Martial a moment before, now hangs his head and cracks his knuckles.

So Quicksilver was out to avenge his father, ten years after! . . . And Sainte-Marie-des-Côtes wipes its collective nose on its shirtsleeve.

Jimmy-the-Flea, who followed Martial to the stand, spent his time turning his head to the back left-hand corner of the courtroom where Crache-à-Pic huddled in the shadows. . . . You didn't see anything, Jimmy, you don't know anything, Dieudonné didn't promise you anything, didn't give you anything, didn't tell you anything. State your name, Christian name, age, and profession . . . a Galosh, that'll make them laugh, loosen them up a bit . . . and that's all. Whatever you do, don't try to play with the court, it's no time to act like a swell . . . you saw just a minute ago what they almost got Martial to say. And this isn't Martial's first trial, not by a long shot. . . . Say nothing at all, Jimmy, and say it all crooked, mix your words up, put the verb in front of the subject, talk through your hat if you like . . . but don't name anyone. . . . Well done, Jimmy, now leave, thank the judge with a nod and go back to your place without looking at the jury.

. . . Little Philias wouldn't be called?

No, Little Philias had been exempted. That was funny, he'd have had plenty of things to say. If there was somebody who knew the bootleggers' life inside out, it was Little Philias. . . . But Philias had already spent some time in a sanatorium and was able to prove to the court that the disease had set in again. And the court judged it wise not to force a man suffering from tuberculosis complicated by consumption to come spitting his testimony out in the judge's face. Especially since the judge had a weak chest, so they said.

But let that pass.

The arrival of the Three Kings put the court into wonderful humour. Even the judge cheered up. For Melchior, Gaspard, and Balthazar took the courtroom for a theatre and the trial for a show. They trooped in with great pomp bearing gold, frankincense, and myrrh.

. . . The truth, the whole truth, and nothing but the truth, so help me God for once in my life.

"Silence! Start over. The oath and nothing else."

The clerk wasn't laughing.

"Swear!"

So Melchior swore.

"Holy Jumping Jesus Christ!"

The court burst into a roar of laughter.

Even the judge understood. He squared himself on his bench, squinted, gave five or six little raps with his mallet, and addressed himself to the court. It was his first speech, precise, sharp, and in a single language — for the interpreter hadn't caught his breath yet. There was no need anyway. He just had to let his eye roam round the room to see that everyone was following. You don't have to be bilingual to understand a reprimand from the bench . . . a serious warning . . . because a trial, ladies and gentlemen, is not a laughing matter, no more than a church service. . . . A man is dead, a duly sworn representative of the law, killed by a bullet, the medical examination established that, therefore there is a murderer, a criminal who must be discovered and judged. The judge mopped his brow . . . don't think for an instant that we are here for amusement, or that the state removes its King's Bench down here among the sand dunes for a masquerade. Justice must be done. And you are here, witnesses and jury, to help the law see that it is done. And blah-blah-blah and blah-blah-blah . . . for forty minutes. Longer than the Sunday sermon. But when silence returned, Melchior understood that he was to speak the truth, the whole truth, and nothing but the truth.

This was the moment Gaspard chose to ask the court's permission to leave the room.

. . . ?

He had to go to the bathroom.

The judge acceded to his request but summoned two uniformed guards to accompany him. Oh no! Not that! Gaspard let the court know that ever since he'd been out of diapers he'd been able to do it all by himself, so help him God!

"Silence! Order in the court!"

Gaspard's absence gave Balthazar free rein to help Melchior with his testimony. Thus every time the first of the Three Kings expressed the truth and nothing but the truth, Balthazar ostensibly denied it with a shake of his head. Which forced the Crown, and the defence, to rephrase the question in the negative.

"You didn't find a schooner drifting out at sea in the sunshine?"

"Nohow."

" . . . ? Don't forget you're under oath."

"I didn't find a schooner drifting out at sea in the sunshine. On account of because when we found her the sun wasn't up yet."

"Hee-hee!"

"Very well then. . . . But you don't deny being the first on the scene where the *Sea-Cow* was drifting?

"I don't deny it."

"Then you affirm it?"

"I don't affirm it."

"But you. . . . "

Melchior opens wide a pair of big haggard eyes.

"Does it have to be absolutely one or the other?"

The Crown restates the question with considerable unction.

"Monsieur Melchior . . . Melchior?"

"That's my real name; the others aren't"

"The others?"

"Gaspard and Balthazar. They're nicknames."

The lawyer rummages in his papers, then gives up.

"Monsieur Witness, did you or did you not, on the twenty-fourth of June, 1933, find a schooner called the *Sea-Cow* floating out at sea?"

"What day is it today?"

"*Oui ou non?* . . . Yes or no?"

"Yes sir!"

He salutes, three fingers to the temple.

"Very good. Now, aboard the schooner . . . the said *Sea-Cow* . . . you follow me?"

"How's that again?"

"I said, do you follow me?"

"Wherever you want."

"So on board the *Sea-Cow*, the said schooner . . . uh . . . that's to say, the said *Sea-Cow*. . . . "

"To say the said what? What was that you said?"

The Crown is on the verge of collapse.

"An offence against the dignity of the court, Your Honour. I request that the witness be brought to order."

So the interpreter shouts, "Order in the court!"

Gaspard, returning at this instant from his extrajudicial mission and still accompanied by his two guards, takes this as an order directed at him personally and springs to attention, which sends the guards bumping into one another and then into Gaspard, who stumbles down three steps and lands against the witness box.

This little diversion relaxes the audience and permits the Crown to readjust and collect its dignity. And the interrogation starts up again.

"Witness number thirteen, I ask you to reply, simply, clearly, and straightforwardly to my question."

"I refuse."

"What's that? . . . This is contempt of court, Your Honour."

"I refuse to be stuck with the number thirteen, it's unlucky."

"Monsieur Melchior, you are not number thirteen, you have just been called to the witness stand in the thirteenth place, that's all."

"Then call another, not me. I'll be number twelve, or number fourteen, but not thirteen. When I was young I knew a man ran his horse wearing the number thirteen one Sunday afternoon, a good horse and all, one of the best, trained by Jing Jang in person. . . . "

The courtroom leans forward, all ears, elbows on their knees.

". . . He'd bought this horse down on a spud farm in Maine, you see, paid cash for him, so they say, and in those days no more than today a horse wasn't to be had just for the asking, especially not a purebred animal, three-quarters Tennessee, one-quarter Morgan, and one-quarter Appaloosa, a real thoroughbred . . . why, ladies, just to look at that trotter was enough to make you sorry you weren't born a mare. . . ."

Thunderous laughter in the courtroom.

The judge consults the interpreter who stammers and jabbers sounds ending in . . . ing, . . . ang, . . . ong to give himself time to catch up with the drift of the story, which is now at the first race, a trotting race, with strong drivers and jangling harness. . . .

"It's a sulky race, Your Honour."

The interpreter has caught up with the storyteller-witness who, after recounting the glorious performance of the best horse ever to set hoof on this coast, ends lamely in front of the stands before a crowd of three thousand people come from everywhere, from Cocagne, Grand-Digue, Pré-d'en-Haut, and Sussex, from everywhere, a crowd that witnessed, it's the witness who says so, the collapse of the champion two seconds from the finish line.

"And all on account of because the horse was wearing the number thirteen, My Honour."

And Melchior mops his brow and salutes the audience, who applaud him roundly.

"Silence!"

"Order in the court!"

At this moment Gaspard raises his hand.

"His Honour! His Honour! I'm not afraid, I'm not superstitious. Let me take his place."

So Gaspard is called to the stand.

But with his first answers the Crown discovers that it has gained nothing in the exchange, for at every question Gaspard refers the court to Melchior.

"I don't know, My Honour, you'd have to ask Melchior, it's him who saw the schooner first and him who was first aboard."

"But you were present too, you saw a young man holding the head of a dead man in his lap?"

"Oh no, My Honour, that's just it, on account of because I had Balthazar right in front of me just as we came alongside, and that big plaid shirt of his blocked my view. Balthazar could tell you, ask him."

So Balthazar steps up. He has exchanged his big plaid shirt for the suit his late father left him on his deathbed, a suit that has accompanied all the married men in his family to the altar. This coquetry has led his two royal friends to rig themselves out in their family treasures too. Parading their regal attributes, the Three Kings present themselves to the court in full wedding trim as well.

So it's with his neck squeezed into a collar stiffened with potato starch and his ankles hanging six inches out of his late father's pants that Balthazar, full of dignity and rectitude and ironed and starched to within an inch of his life, takes the stand.

"The truth, the whole truth, and nothing but the truth," trumpets Balthazar, at which the Bible slips out of the clerk's hand and falls open at the story of Joshua at the battle of Jericho.

At least this one won't try to be smart, thinks the Crown attorney. Looks like a good head. Feet planted firm on the ground. Not the kind to split hairs or play around with words.

"Are your Pierre or Paul?"

"Pierre-Paul."

"Very well."

Clear, direct, a good head.

"You participated with your comrades in the rescue of a vessel in distress. . . . "

"With me, His Honour, you'd be better off to say straight out what it is you've got to say, without using all those big words. 'Rescue', I know that, and 'vessel' . . . but 'comrades in distress' . . . ."

"Very well, then. You were out at sea, you saw a ship, you rowed towards it, you climbed on board, you looked around, and you saw — what?"

Balthazar has been following carefully and seems satisfied. He smiles at the Crown, tosses back his shock of hair, and says,

"I was at sea, I saw a ship, I rowed towards it, I climbed on board, I looked around, and I saw that the mast was broken."

" . . . And then?"

"That sail was hanging down. It was torn into shreds."

"Is that all?"

"I saw you'd never be able to mend it and Crache-à-Pic would have to get another."

"Don't forget, Pierre-Paul, that you swore. . . ."

"Me? I never did! I said to Melchior and Gaspard, 'That sail's had it.' I didn't even say, 'By Jeez.' "

"You swore to the court to tell the truth."

"That's the truth. I don't remember swearing."

"And what did you see besides a broken mast and a torn sail?"

"My pants. . . ."

"I beg your pardon?"

"Excuse me, My Honour, but my pants are ripping. Can I have permission to step outside a second?"

The courtroom breaks up into laughter so loud you can't hear the blows of the mallet on the judge's desk. The clerk, the guards, and the lawyers for the defence and the Crown are waving their arms like tentacles more numerous than the arms of a Hindu goddess. And Balthazar — tight-assed, his hands masking the split — makes off down the aisle with tiny steps like a ballerina trying to hide her bum.

Called back to the stand as witness number fifteen, Melchior finally explains that neither he nor his friends saw Ti-Louis and Quicksilver right away . . .

" . . . on account of because the sail had dropped over them."

Once the veil of the sail had been lifted, Melchior had nothing more to hide and revealed everything: Ti-Louis's dirge, which he had never ceased playing all the time the fishermen were hauling the schooner in to port; Quicksilver's white face, even more handsome than when he was alive, with a thread of blood dividing it from forehead to chin; and the *Sea-Cow* groaning and moaning like a chorus of mourners at a shrouded bedside during a wake.

The court wasn't laughing any more, not moving either; their eyes were lowered to their knees, and their nostrils took in the air in short, noisy, rapid breaths.

There weren't all that many witnesses left; the judge began to collect his papers and the lawyers fidgeted and eyed each other on the sly. The crowd didn't dare look towards the accused's box. Sooner or later. . . .

They called Joe Colossus to the stand. Even the judge seemed impressed. Joe was longer than His Honour's father and grandfather laid end to end. A single man didn't even reach up to the giant's lower ribs; it took two, one on the other's shoulders, to talk to him face to face. Yes, the judge was impressed. And to swear him in the clerk had to hold the Bible over his head at arm's length.

The swearing-in took a long time. The giant didn't seem to know what was going on. Everybody knew it wasn't Joe who put the legs on flies, or the springs in grasshoppers' legs — nobody was expecting to hear him set out a speech in tidy sentences, subject, verb, object. But you'd have thought he'd at least be able to talk, to say things like, 'I didn't see anything, I wasn't there, I don't know anything about it, I couldn't say. . . . ' But no! Nothing. He couldn't remember his own name. A kind of jargon came out of this ogre's mouth, a garble of prrrt . . . and gnnna . . . and stchchpt. . . .

"Get him out!" shouted the judge.

At any rate, Joe Colossus wouldn't have been able to add much to what his master and accomplice, Black Willy, the principal witness, had to say. Nobody expected much of Joe except the Crown, who would have been glad to push him into contradicting Black Willy, or even. . . . But the whole courtroom began to shift around on their fannies, as if to tell the judge it was high time to take the bull by the horns.

And the bull stepped forward.

Black Willy.

. . . the truth, the whole truth, and nothing but the truth, so help me God.

"Name, Christian name, age, and profession."

Now that was really too much; the courtroom noisily gave vent to its displeasure. Get down to the facts! They wanted a story, a drama, all the circumstances of the tragedy as it had unfolded out there on the high seas on the eve of La Saint-Jean, right down to the last words of the dying man. . . .

. . . Come on now! The accused isn't even convicted yet and already you want the details of the murder. Black Willy is nothing but a witness like the others . . . well, no, not like the others, but a witness just the same. He's not the accused; he wasn't at the helm that night; the *Kouchibougouac* isn't his ship; the only guilty party, if there is one, is the captain. It's odd that on the eve of La Saint-Jean Dieudonné was at the wheel of his Scottish Fisherman . . . quite a boat, that! It's odd because ordinarily Dieudonné lets his men go out alone. . . . Well, this is a piece of luck for Black Willy; he won't have to take the rap for what happened.

"At what time did you put out to sea on the twenty-third of June?"

"Eight o'clock."

"And what time did you come back?"

"Eleven."

"What were you doing out there in the middle of the night?"

"It was evening. We were testing a new motor."

"Why did you need a new motor?"

"The other one wasn't working."

"What is the *Kouchibougouac* used for?"

"The lumber business."

"You carry lumber on a Scottish Fisherman?"

"No, it's for the business end, for contacting buyers, that kind of stuff."

"You had business the night in question?"

"As usual."

"With whom?"

"Some guy from the north."

"His name?"

"He didn't say."

"What time did you meet him?"

"At . . . ten."

"Where?"

"In the north."

"The north's a big place."

"Off l'Anse-aux-Outardes."

"After that you came straight back?"

"That's right."

"Around by the dune?"

"Yes."

"At what time did you come round by the dune?"

"Ten-thirty."

"How long does it take a new motor to come from the dune into harbour at Sainte-Marie-des-Côtes?"

"Half an hour."

"So you were back home at eleven o'clock?"

Black Willy flashes the smile of a general watching an enemy in retreat.

"And your motor?"

"How's that? . . . "

"The *Kouchibougouac*'s new motor, how did it work?"

"Oh . . . fine. A good buy. A Bessamer. First class."

"So that's what allowed you to get as far as l'Anse-aux-Outardes?"

"We could have gone past Négouac Point and as far as Caraquet if we'd opened her up. A real good buy, I can tell you."

"And your guy from the north, what did he think of it?"

. . . ?

"What did he have to say about the Bessamer, your contact from l'Anse-aux-Outardes?"

"Well, uh. . . . "

"Was it to have a new motor checked that the *Kouchibougouac* went north to meet a lumber buyer at l'Anse-aux-Outardes?"

Black Willy glances nervously at the accused's box. Dieudonné is studying his knees.

"Did you go out on lumber business, or to test a new motor?"

" . . . Both. Two birds with one stone."

"Nothing else?"

"What do you mean?"

"Not three birds with one stone, for example?"

"No."

"And you saw nothing out at sea?"

"Nothing."

"What time did you leave port?"

"Eight o'clock."

. . . He won't catch me . . . eight o'clock. I've said it twice now . . . back at eleven . . . he won't catch me.

"Do you have witnesses?"

. . . Witnesses? . . . The Damien boys . . . the Damien boys were building a barn for their father that night.

"The Damien boys saw us passing not far from their place."

"And where is their place?"

"At the Cocagne bar."

"So you left by the south to go north?"

Black Willy fidgets, stammers, then gets hold of himself.

"To test the engine."

"Of course. Southern waters are better for testing engines."

Black Willy takes out his handkerchief and pretends to blow his nose. But the Crown sees him mopping his forehead.

"Aside from your commercial contact, you met no one out at sea?"

"Nobody."

"Not even the *Sea-Cow*?

"Never saw her."

"Yet she came round the dune about ten."

"No, not at ten."

" . . . How do you know?"

"I know because I was there at ten and I would have seen her."

He smiles again. The enemy is in full flight.

"Listen carefully, Willy, and don't forget that you are under oath."

Black Willy grips the rail and clenches his teeth. . . . Don't let yourself be distracted, Willy, open your ears, don't let them make you talk. . . .

"I repeat: you didn't see anyone out at sea on the night of the twenty-third of June?"

"Nobo. . . ."

He stops . . . don't trip yourself up, Willy. If you didn't see anybody, the *Kouchibougouac* was alone at sea.

"I saw a boat."

The courtroom holds its breath.

"What boat? Don't forget, you are under oath."

There is a stir in the accused's box. Dieudonné is demanding to be heard. The accused wishes to give evidence! The courtroom is like a kettle on the boil.

"Let the accused take the stand."

Make way, make way. Silence. Order in the court. Dieudonné steps forward. Tall and dignified. Head high. He walks straight up to the box.

The women cross themselves. The men move restlessly. The jury looks elsewhere. The defence attorney smiles at his client. The court clerk clears his lungs.

"Do you swear to tell the truth, the whole truth, and nothing but the truth, so help you God?"

"I do."

He's sworn it.

"You were at sea on the night of the twenty-third of June?"

"I was at sea."

"Alone or with others?"

"With others: Joe and Willy."

"Who was in command?"

"Me."

. . . There. He's said it. He can't go back on that now.

"When you were out at sea, did you meet another ship?"

"Yes."

"Did you recognize it?"

"Yes."

"It was someone you knew, since you admit you recognized the ship."

"That's so."

"Someone you had arranged to meet."

"Right."

The judge leans forward.

"The court demands to know the name of the ship and its captain."

Dieudonné slightly crinkles his left eye, his eye for grand occasions, as Black Willy used to call it.

Then he replies to the court in a clear voice,

"Al Capone on the *Dragon*."

The lid blows off the kettle.

. . . Well! The devil take it! Where did you ever fish that one up, Dieudonné? Al Capone! Nobody's ever going to get *him* into court. Not into court at Sainte-Marie-des-Côtes, at any rate. The judge can twiddle his wig and call on his King's Bench till the cows come home. Good work, Dieudonné!

After this deposition the defence had a ball. It was child's play. The question became who had seen Al Capone first, Dieudonné or Black Willy; who had heard the first shot, never suspecting, of course, that the *Sea-Cow* was out there too; and the cross-examination ended with the suggestion that they had thought they were being fired upon, and so had hurried back by way of the dune.

. . . Bravo, Dieudonné! A shade more and the court would have burst into applause.

Order in the court.

One key witness remained, the one who had brought the victim's corpse back in the decapitated schooner. Ti-Louis the Whistler.

Dieudonné's terror.

Yet Black Willy had tried to calm his chief: Ti-Louis came from the States, he was a stranger, a fuzzy-minded youngster, the artist-type, and he hadn't opened his mouth since that fatal day. Doubtless he hadn't seen anything, there was no moon, the only light had come from the stars. . . . What was the word of a single witness, a young vagabond into the bargain, who'd fallen out with his uncle, had even beaten him up one night — Black Willy had this from Célestine's man himself — a kid who'd apparently served time in American prisons, too — or at least in reformatories for juvenile delinquents — before he'd even set foot in this country. No, Dieudonné, a witness like that doesn't weigh more than a feather in the balance against an honourable man like you!

Two uniformed guards push Ti-Louis into the witness box. They forcibly put his hand on the Bible . . . so help you God.

God and Crache-à-Pic.

. . . The artist-type, eh? You're right, Black Willy. Ti-Louis is the magician who hears sounds through his throat, his nose, the pores of his skin. He doesn't need ears to hear or eyes to see. He has felt Crache-à-Pic hidden there in the shadow of her shadow, but he hasn't turned his head towards the back left-hand corner of the room even once. He knows.

And he doesn't speak.

"You were on the ship? On deck? In the hold? Never mind. You must have heard the shot, heard talking, shouting. . . ."

. . . .

"Why were you with the victim that night?"

. . . .

Have you been in the country long?"

. . . .

"Do you have friends here?"

. . . .

"How old are you? . . . What's your name? . . ."

. . . .

"I think, Your Honour, that it is useless to carry on this questioning," the defence concludes.

But the Crown insists.

"He has a tongue, after all; the court hasn't certified him a deaf-mute."

"According to inquiry, he has not spoken a word since the event. Struck dumb. *In stuporem attonitus*, Your Honour."

. . . This gives the interpreter a coughing fit. You must admit it's asking a lot of the poor man. Doubtless nobody warned him that he'd be called on to translate Latin as well. But His Honour is still waiting for the end of the sentence; he doesn't seem to have registered the switch in languages.

The Crown makes a new attempt.

"This is a prime witness, Your Honour."

The defence tries to have Ti-Louis excused.

"It's a case of traumatic shock to the frontal lobe. *Dementia praecox*. Insanity, Your Honour."

. . . Hey! Hey! Watch it, Mr. Lawyer! As much Latin as you want, but insanity . . . you're going too far!

The judge leans forward and says a word in the ear of the doctor from Sainte-Marie-des-Côtes, who has been called

302

to the stand; then he gives three nervous little smacks of his mallet, as though playing a tambourine, and makes a garbled noise. The interpreter unscrambles this to:

"Incompetent."

. . . The doctor must have found the proper disease for Ti-Louis, because they let him leave the court without a further word spoken.

The Crown scowls, the defence smiles, the accused sighs. . . . Catch your breath, Dieudonné, take a deep one. It's over. That scoundrel Black Willy was right after all: Al Capone's shoulders are broad enough . . . he'll know how to take care of himself. . . . The case is closed.

. . . There's a stir in the courtroom, over there — at the back, in the corner. Someone is asking to take the stand. Let them through.

Crache-à-Pic!

She is in the box, the clerk presents the Bible, she swears, omits "so help me God". . . . Silence! Order in the court! Superfluous request . . . you could hear a fly land. But the clerk must have been alarmed . . . or the judge . . . or the interpreter . . . certainly the defence. The lawyer signals the accused to stay calm. Nobody move now. Crache-à-Pic has seen nothing, heard nothing, said nothing since. . . . That's just it, she hasn't said anything yet . . . hasn't spoken since. . . . Shh! Quiet.

"So help you God. Swear."

"I swear."

. . . Name, Christian name, age, profession. . . . Hurry up, get on to her testimony.

"Your Honour, on the eve of La Saint-Jean, Al Capone was not at sea."

That's all. Not a word more. She's made her statement. A subject, a verb, a complement. Now it's the whole courtroom that's struck dumb, afflicted with *stuporem attonitus*. Even Dieudonné. He's not sure he understood; he's holding his ear as if the bullet pierced his eardrum now, two months later.

The Crown leans forward, wants clarifications.

"How do you know this? . . . Take your time, answer slowly."

She has taken her time all right. All summer long. . . .

"I know because I was the one who told him not to come, that the rendezvous was cancelled. I warned Al Capone."

"And how did you do that?"

"By telegraph, Dieudonné's telegraph, buried under the hay in his barn."

She knew the smugglers' code — *dog, chair, pigeon, bird* — Quicksilver had entrusted it to her the night before the crime. She wanted revenge. On Dieudonné. And on the constable a little, for going to sea without her . . . on her own *Sea-Cow*.

"Is that all you have to say?"

"That's all."

And she went back down the aisle as she had come up it, her feet barely touching the ground.

After Crache-à-Pic left the courtroom the crowd, which had been holding its breath, exploded. The flies realized it was time to get back to their places. The Three Kings, Marie-Pet, Jeannette, Xavier-the-Hunchback, Long-Tongue Médard, all Sainte-Marie-des-Côtes, Bois-Joli, Champdoré, Cocagne, Village-des-Trois-Maisons — all of them, the healthy, the halt, the sick, and the lame, they all blew the silence in the court into a thousand pieces. The judge clasped his wig, the lawyers their briefs, the clerk his Bible, shouting, "Order in the court!"

. . . As Dieudonné struggled out of his bewilderment, his eyes sank to his knees. . . . She's got me.

The jury was at last requested to retire, after long speeches by the defence and the Crown . . . not too long, just long enough. The latter insisted on the accused's false testimony and on the fact that only one ship besides the *Sea-Crow* had gone out to sea that night. The former repeated: no proof, no proof . . . and then went on to speak of Dieudonné-the-honourable-man. Never hurt a fly, has his own pew in church, family man, no debts, no past history, no police record . . . his character as white as a sheet.

The lawyer was right, Dieudonné was white as a sheet all right. A pitiful sight.

. . . But the judge had warned us, all twelve: no pity. Neither compassion nor malice. Neutral, that's the way he wanted us, and just. . . . You have heard the witnesses, the defence, and the Crown; hereafter the full weight of the verdict, guilty or not guilty, rests with you. It is for you to judge. According to your conscience. And after due reflection.

Not so easy. Not the due reflection part, no problem there, we'd been reflecting for weeks. But the conscience bit. Everybody had his own and had to come to terms with it. Twelve jurors, twelve consciences. The court required a unanimous decision, that's what His Honour said. And to get that unanimity the court had gone and chosen three babblers from Champdoré, two half-wits from Cocagne, one sniveller from Trois-Maisons, four smart-alecs from Grand-Digue, a crippled-up old gaffer from Sainte-Marie-

des-Côtes, and me — the last two being the only ones with a
head on their shoulders. No wonder they elected me foreman, it was between me and one of those scatterbrains from
Grand-Digue.

. . . Don't go thinking it went to my head. Foreman . . .
pooh! Everyone knows the story of how the asshole got
elected boss. But foreman of a jury, that's a responsibility. I
mean, to judge a man, a neighbour with a wife and children.
And his own pew in church . . . Jehosaphat! Guildor, judge
however you like but don't fly off the handle. No malice,
that's what the judge told us. And whatever you do, don't
let local rivalry get mixed up in it. Just because the harbour
at Cocagne has barely ten feet of water at low tide . . . all
right, twelve. . . . Don't forget, there's the life of a man and
neighbour at stake . . . I know, Théophile, he wasn't everyone's
neighbour, but even if you do come from Champdoré he's
still your neighbour, like the Bible says. Guilty or not guilty,
that's the only question. So everybody swallow back their
bile and keep their grudges to themselves. Guilty or not
guilty. . . . There's the false testimony, yes, Crache-à-Pic's
deposition showed that up clearly enough. And the Crown
confirmed her evidence the day after, with proof from Al
Capone's headquarters in Chicago. . . . Quite a woman, that
Crache-à-Pic! Her ancestors would be proud. Her voice didn't
tremble, she held her head up straight and tall, she said
what she had to say, not a word more, without a wrinkle on
her brow . . . the accused himself might have thought she
was seeing him for the first time. But her statement didn't
leave the shadow of a doubt. It wasn't Al Capone who fired
the shot. Therefore, false testimony. . . . That's true, sure
enough, but since when do we go around hanging a man
for false testimony? Guilty or not guilty of the death of

Quicksilver, Mathieu-Martin Vigneault. A man is dead, that's
the only thing sure and certain. Dead from a bullet in the
forehead. The bullet was found, but not the gun. Died in
harness, that's a good death. . . . What are you talking about?
I'd say a strapping young fellow like Quicksilver would prefer
a good life to a good death any day, and him only thirty-
three years old. Especially since for the past year. . . . Yessir!
He had a good life all right, the constable did. But you have
to feel sorry for those who are left behind. I wonder why
Crache-à-Pic didn't talk, didn't let the Little Whistler talk
. . . she must have her reasons. Why no, Julien, the said
Ti-Louis isn't suffering from atonal stupidity or any other
kind of contagious disease, he kept his trap shut of his own
free will, he knew exactly what he was doing. Voluntarily,
that's right. And the proof is . . . you want proof? Just let me
out of this dog-house and you'll see what's left of his *dementia
praecox*. . . . Does that mean that if Ti-Louis had talked . . . ?
It doesn't mean any such thing. Since he didn't talk.
You don't hang a man for an *if*. Clovis is right. Thanks,
Thomas. . . . It's getting hot in this chicken coop. Sooner or
later these twelve men are going to have to speak the same
language, each in turn, and share the same . . . priorities.
There's Dieudonné — a bootlegger, a profiteer, a crook.
Underhand in everything, a fox, a wolf who's fleeced every
sheep on the coast. But a neighbour nevertheless, born in
these parts, of the same family tree as. . . . And after all, it's
the law that's after him, not Quicksilver or Crache-à-Pic. If
Crache-à-Pic had wanted to, all she'd have had to do was
whistle for the Whistler, he would have told everything. Yet
Quicksilver was the love of her life. And Dieudonné was
her worst enemy, and her mother's too, and all the Crache-
à-Pics'. I just wonder if . . . but all she said was "Your Honour,

Al Capone wasn't at sea that night." As for the rest, nothing. So how are we supposed to be able to. . . . Great God in Heaven! You're right, Pierre-à-Tom, they could damn well have gone and chosen somebody else for their jury!

After two days and three nights the jury did know which of the twelve snored lowest in the octave; who ground his teeth in his sleep; who farted baked beans and with what smell; who held a personal grudge against Dieudonné, and who against Quicksilver; who didn't mind seeing Crache-à-Pic unattached again . . . you never know, sometimes a woman forgets . . . ; who would have preferred to be out lobster-fishing (the season had been open for two weeks); who was drooping and dying of boredom; who dreamt of his wife snug in her feather-bed in the early hours of the morning; who was calculating on his fingers so many days' appearance in the jury box at so much a day; who tried to sort out all the pros and cons; and who, finally, asked to be heard; it was the little crippled-up old gaffer who hadn't opened his mouth once during all their deliberations.

"And what if we said . . . ."

The eleven others leaned across the table to hear the sentence proposed by the most toothless, the most cavernous, yet the cleanest mouth on the whole of the coast.

It was Clovis, as foreman of the jury, who was charged to reply in the name of the twelve unanimous men to the question posed by the court: guilty or not guilty? So Clovis looked the judge straight in the eye, raised his hand high — the palm held flat open so that all Sainte-Marie-des-Côtes and its suburbs would recognize the hand they'd so often seen stamped on a gallon of Hand Brand — and spoke the verdict:

"He died by somebody's hand."

And while the judge declared a mistrial, the whole country, which during that summer of 1933 had lived out the greatest emotional adventure in its history, broke into a roar of laughter.

Old Clovis would never admit to my father that he didn't know who went looking for whom — Dieudonné for Crache-à-Pic, or vice versa. But that wasn't important anyway. They saw each other. And spoke. On the run-down wharf at Cap-Lumière, in the shadow of the broken mast of the *Sea-Cow*.

She said to him,

"You know what you have to do."

He didn't reply but hung his head.

"You're going to leave, get out of this country without taking anything with you. I'll make this perfectly clear, Dieudonné — you must never again set foot on this coast. Because the day you do, Ti-Louis will shout out to every dune and cliff the words that remain seared in his eardrum: 'Dieudonné, you've killed Quicksilver! Dieudonné, you've killed Quicksilver! . . . ' "

He moved one hand and opened his mouth to . . . but closed it without saying anything. This time she really had got him. He wouldn't swing from the end of a rope, no. Even Crache-à-Pic didn't want to go to sleep every night with a vision like that in her head. But he would live in exile. He would have to begin again somewhere else . . . and . . . but at sixty it would be too late. The bitch knew it all too well.

She had avenged her Quicksilver handsomely.

She had avenged the whole country, too. Aglaé could close her eyes in her grave now. And the old sorcerer Crache-à-Pic could rest quiet in his hole under the apple tree for a long eternity.

Thirty years later, the children of Sainte-Marie-des-Côtes are still going into Dieudonné's abandoned fields to pick strawberries and currants and wild gooseberries. And as for the weathercock of the world. . . .

"You should never give the little devil his head," said Old Clovis to my father. "You never can tell what unbridled winds can stir up in a hearth in the way of sand and straw and live embers. And in the world we live in today, it doesn't take much to set things afire."

Finished at the lighthouse, September 8, 1983,
on the feast of Sainte-Marie-des-Côtes

If you have enjoyed this book and would like to receive details of other Walker Adventure titles, please write to:

Adventure Editor
Walker and Company
720 Fifth Avenue
New York, NY 10019